Steal not this book for fear of shame
For here you see the owner's name
And when you die, the Lord will say,
"Where is that book you stole away?"
And you will say, you do not know
And He will say, "Go down below".

COCKATOO
SOUP

HODDER AND STOUGHTON
SYDNEY AUCKLAND LONDON TORONTO

COCKATOO SOUP

Jean Chapman
illustrated by
Rodney McRae

For permission to use copyright material we thank the following:

Angus and Robertson Publishers for permission to reprint: "Singing the Knees" by Mary Gilmore from *The Passionate Heart*. © Estate of the late Mary Gilmore, 1948 and 1969; an extract from *The Magic Pudding* by Norman Lindsay © Janet Glad, 1918; an extract from *The Complete Aventures of Blinky Bill* by Dorothy Wall © Angus and Robertson, 1939; an extract from an appendix to the story, *The Little Black Princess* by Mrs Aeneas Gunn © Dr Harry A. Derham, 1905.

Associated Book Publishers (UK) Ltd, Methuen London for "The Children's Crusade" from *Tales from the Calendar* by Bertolt Brecht translated by Michael Hamburger.

The Aeroplane Jelly Company for "Aeroplane Jelly Song"

Berndt, Prof. R.M. for "The Evening Star" song presented here in a modified way comes from Song 13 of "A Wonguri-Manjikai song cycle of the Moonbon" published in *Oceania*, 1948, Vol XIX, No. 1.

Exley Publications for "Our Tomorrow" by Sally Atkins from *Cry for our Beautiful World* edited by Helen Exley, © 1985 Exley Publications Ltd.

Jacaranda Wiley Ltd. for "Biami", "Corroboree" and extract from "Bora" from *My People* by Kath Walker.

Scott, W.N. for "Little Tom Thumb" © W.N. Scott.

The publishers have made every effort to trace copyright holders, in some cases without success. We would be grateful to hear from any copyright holders not here acknowledged.

First published in 1987
by Hodder and Stoughton (Australia) Pty Ltd
2 Apollo Place, Lane Cove, NSW 2066
© text Jean Chapman 1987
© illustrations Rodney McRae 1987
© music settings Hodder and Stoughton (Australia) Pty Limited
This book is copyright. Apart from any fair dealing for the purposes of private study, research, criticism or review, as permitted under the Copyright Act, no part may be reproduced by any process without written permission. Inquiries should be addressed to the publishers.
National Library of Australia Cataloguing-in-Publication entry
Chapman, Jean
 Cockatoo Soup
 For Children
ISBN 0 340 40383 7 Hardback
I. Children's Literature. I. McRae, Rodney. II Title
Typeset in Century Light by Dovatype, Melbourne.
Printed in Hong Kong.

INTRODUCTION

This collection was three years in the making. Often we wished that we could include more and more material from the rising pile that had accumulated rapidly. But I realise now that it was not a collection limited to that period, but a lifetime of collecting that included books from my own childhood and things I could not bear to throw out. However, when it came to making a final choice of work there was an initial priority — that it must be meaningful to contemporary children. As well, there was an important need for chronological order — for authenticity, logic and overall shape. It was to be a sharing — wunnun.

Most of the stories and songs, rhymes and activities are reproduced as they were known to previous generations, except for a few noted simplifications or retellings such as the stories, *Tom Thumbe* and *Elidor*, and in these adaptations as much as possible of the original text has been retained.

Hopefully, this book will encourage children to read more widely and enlarge their interest in the children who went before them. For some knowledge of their past will help them to understand the present and to create for the future. The collection could become a personal one, particularly if the family origin is other than Aboriginal or British. Migrations to Australia from diverse nationalities have increased in recent years and in our limited space we could only afford to generalise, although aware that many influences from many sources have enriched our society and culture. We made our decision with difficulties and heart-searches and the result will attract criticism, no doubt. Fortunately, children are much less conscious of racial differences than adults and the future is theirs.

Enjoy our book.

Jean Chapman

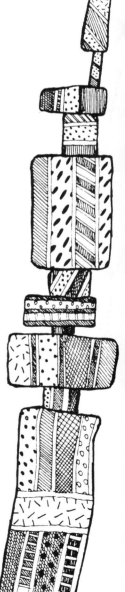

For Eve
and
Juliana Bayfield
and
for
you

CONTENTS

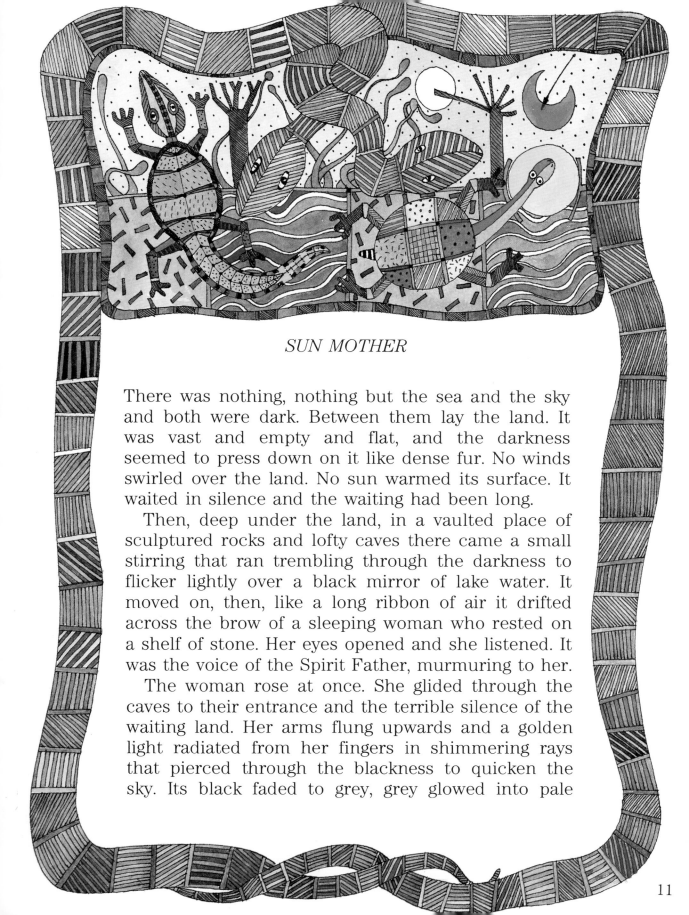

SUN MOTHER

There was nothing, nothing but the sea and the sky and both were dark. Between them lay the land. It was vast and empty and flat, and the darkness seemed to press down on it like dense fur. No winds swirled over the land. No sun warmed its surface. It waited in silence and the waiting had been long.

Then, deep under the land, in a vaulted place of sculptured rocks and lofty caves there came a small stirring that ran trembling through the darkness to flicker lightly over a black mirror of lake water. It moved on, then, like a long ribbon of air it drifted across the brow of a sleeping woman who rested on a shelf of stone. Her eyes opened and she listened. It was the voice of the Spirit Father, murmuring to her.

The woman rose at once. She glided through the caves to their entrance and the terrible silence of the waiting land. Her arms flung upwards and a golden light radiated from her fingers in shimmering rays that pierced through the blackness to quicken the sky. Its black faded to grey, grey glowed into pale

11

rose, then flushed pink, then gold. The gold stretched and spread and grew and burst like an explosion into the brilliance of the first day. The Sun Mother had brought life to the waiting land.

She breathed deeply. A stream of air funnelled skywards to summon the winds. They came quickly, ruffling the sea, scattering sand and swirling dust. Then, as if unable to be still they rushed off in all directions to seek clouds and rain.

The Sun Mother almost followed them with dancing steps and where her feet touched the ground grass blades sprang from the dry earth. They were followed by shrubs and trees and all manner of green things and she knew that she must now begin a great journey. She strode across the land giving it colour but it was as if it still waited for something more. She laughed, remembering what she must do. Now as she walked she threw up mountains, pushed down gorges, sliced rock into cliffs. She kicked rocks into piles, rolled out hills and cleaved valleys, dug pools and billabongs and gouged out lakes. Then she paused to look for small creatures and found them slumbering in hidden places. The Sun Mother poked at balls of fur and whispered into limp ears. The land was theirs, she said. She stirred life into insects until the air hummed with bees and flies and the fluttering wings of butterflies and whirring beetles. Her fingers found crevices and holes, startling goannas and lizards. And she prodded lazy snakes until they slithered away from her.

The Sun Mother smiled and called up the waters. They came as fast as the winds, tumbling and rushing to fill the snakes' tracks, that became creeks and rivers in search of the sea.

Fish found the Sun Mother's water places. Frogs croaked. Mosquitoes buzzed. The land is yours, she told them and she created the birds. "Fly with the winds," called the Sun Mother as she threw them high into the air. They soared upwards and she followed their flight to travel the sky, to move from east to west. Her face burned. It was ablaze with light but suddenly, she sank into the sea. Her work was done. The Sun Mother was gone.

Fear gripped the land. Every creature felt alone, deserted. Some wept for her. Some wept for themselves as a darkness crept upon them with the first night, and the night brought terror. Some creatures dug holes and hid. Others huddled on branches, whimpering. Owls screeched and possums screamed for the Sun Mother to return. When she did not a stillness slowly brought sleep for many but Possum and Wombat stayed wide-eyed, snuffling and watchful.

Even so, it was the birds who rejoiced loudly when the Sun Mother returned, although Possum and Wombat must have seen her fingers grip the edge of the sky as she slowly pulled herself upwards to warm feathers and fur. The birds' joy was so loud it woke the sleepers and when they complained that she had left them alone she laughed. "I gave you the gift of rest," she told them and ordered them to drink at the watering places.

Each day she made her journey across the sky. There were the doubtful ones who refused to sleep

when she was gone from them but she always returned. They slept then while she walked across the sky and it became a habit which some follow to this day. So tells the story from the Kurraru People. They also tell that the Sun Mother gave birth to a little son. She called him Morning Star. He grew strong and married the Moon, and their children are the Aborigines who came to live in the land.

GIFTS FROM THE SPIRIT PEOPLE

The Sun Mother's story belonged to many generations of children born to the Karraru in South Australia. In other parts of the country children heard stories that were especially theirs and told of the creation of the land by ancestral spirits. Some of the stories overlap. Others are very different. It depended upon where the people lived and their language, but in all the stories life began in the Dreaming. It was the spirits who shaped the land and gave the gifts of tribal laws and skills, their way of life and the changing seasons with food for the people. None of this was written down but stored in memories as stories, songs and dances, painting, ritual and ceremonies.

The ancestral spirits who behaved as people did not always look like people. The Sun Mother of the Karraru emerged from the secret caverns under the Nullarbor Plains but others rose from the sea. In the far north the Rainbow Serpent heaved out of the ground while on the coast of New South Wales Biami descended from the sky where he returned when his work was over. In Kath Walker's verse a little boy questions his mother about Biami.

BIAMI

"Mother, what is that one sea,
Sometimes blue or green or yellow?"
"That Biami's waterhole.
He big fellow."

"Mother, what makes sunset fire,
Every night the big red glare?"
"Biami's gunyah out that way,
That his camp fire over there."

"How come great wide river here,
Where we swim and fish with spear?"
"Biami dug him.
You see big hills all about?
They the stuff that he chuck out."

Kath Walker

THE VOICE OF BIAMI

The deep voice of Biami can be heard in the
whir of the sacred bull roarer as it makes its
music for rituals or dance.

The bull roarer is carved from a piece of
wood that tapers at both ends and is rubbed
until it is petal smooth.

A hole, bored through the smaller end,
holds a string of human hair. The loop is
swung head high, faster and faster to make
the sound that warns women and children
away from a ritual or ceremony.

The bull roarer can be painted or carved
with beautiful abstract designs.

BABY

A newly-born child was welcomed by his people as well as his parents. The child, as well as being a member of a family and clan, also had a totem of a sacred animal or another creature.

Some tribes rejoiced by laying fire-warmed hands upon the baby. While each part of the child's body was gently touched a blessing was chanted with the hope that the baby would grow strong in body and tribal laws.

The tribes didn't stay in the same camp for long periods, so a new baby travelled with his people, carried in a sling or a coolamon that was a shallow dish of bark with a rounded bottom. The baby's light-coloured skin was rubbed with animal fat then dusted with fine ashes as a protection against sunburn.

Children wore no clothing. Moss or sand lined the coolamon and could be quickly changed when needed.

The baby was praised by everyone and encouraged to join other children as soon as possible. Toddlers learned by watching and imitating other children and adults and so the skills of survival often were taught through play.

SINGING THE KNEES

Be strong, be strong, little knees!
Strong is the bird,
The emu bird,
Be strong as the bird, little knees!

Swift, be swift, little knees!
Swift is the bird,
The emu bird,
Be swift as the bird, little knees!

Wise, wise is the bird,
The emu bird;
Be wise like the bird, little knees,
Be wise.

In the day's march be strong,
Through the wide rivers be strong,
Climbing the mountain be strong,
In the long stalking of foeman or quarry
Be strong, endure as the bird, little knees,
Endure as the bird.

I have sung you,
Sung you the song of the bird;
As the voice of the emu bird
I have sung you strength,
Endure and be strong, little knees.

Mary Gilmore

GAMES

Memory game

You could try this game for yourself. An adult
showed a toddler a single grass blade, or a
tiny stick. It was tossed to the ground. The
child searched to find the grass or stick and
then returned it. One special grass blade
amongst many! Eyes needed to be sharp. It's
not as easy as it sounds.

Observation game

An observation game was to place small
objects in a circle on the ground. There
could be a sliver of bark, several differently
shaped and coloured stones, various leaves,
sticks, bones, even flowers. The child took a
quick look at the objects that were then
swept from sight. The little player named as
many as possible. Try that. Soon you'll be
noticing many small things about you, things
you previously overlooked.

Spear Play

Aboriginal children would have owned few
toys. They may have had a small spear and a
little shield or a boomerang. Children played
with whatever was handy. A disc of bark
could be rolled along the ground then
speared before it lost its balance. They had
stone tops and balls for rolling and tossing,
catching and kicking. The balls were made
from scraps of fur or grass tied into a round
shape with string made from hair or grass or
roots.

Ball of grass

Find some long grass and bend the seed
heads down. Twist and roll the grass over
and over the heads into a ball shape.
You may need help to tie extra grass about
the ball. Use plenty to keep the ball together.
The Aborigines' grass ball was light and didn't
last long but children made them large
enough and strong enough to play a kind of
football. When the ball fell to pieces another
one was quickly made. The skill was to keep
the ball in the air and not touch it with one's
hands.

Dolls

Some people made dolls by carving bark or
wood into a doll shape.
Some dolls were made from fur.
It was tied into a doll shape
with the fur inside. Faces were painted on
with clay.
A knobbled piece of wood could become a
doll. And children modelled mud dolls, giving
them bark cradles.

Seeds, shells and spinifex gum

Both boys and girls liked to wear necklaces, head bands, armlets or anklets. They were made from shells or seeds, teeth, small animal bones, feathers or flowers. Sometimes it would be a combination of these, or colourful seeds set in bees-wax. It took a long time to grind holes into objects to be threaded.

You could make a necklace from seeds or shells you've collected. However, you'll need a grown-up to help to drill holes large enough to thread your treasures on a cord or leather thong, even string. Paint them if you want to do that, but many seeds and shells look best left natural. Find interesting shapes. You may like to glue two or more shapes together. Use strong glue. Aboriginal children made glue from blobs of spinifex gum that was heated over a fire.

Cat's cradle

A favourite game was cat's cradle. All that was needed was a length of twine. Some of the patterns were very complex and the children used both teeth and hands to make them.

The basic position is to hold hands a little apart with fingers pointing upwards.

Loop the string over thumbs and stretch hands apart.

Pick up the string with both little fingers.

With your pointer finger on one hand pick up the string between your thumb and little finger.

Pull back Pointer with the string.

Repeat this movement using the other hand.

And there's the cat's cradle. There are many other patterns you can make once you understand the basic movement.

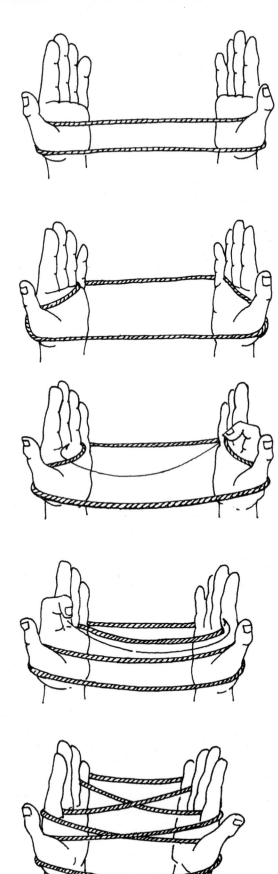

Hand talk

Children watched adults making and repairing tools and they too became skilled. They also learned *hand talk* signals that were used while hunting when absolute silence was necessary.

Wit-wit stick

In the Lake Eyre district of South Australia a *wit-wit*, or play stick, was thrown so that it skipped over hard ground. Have a go at that but be sure that you are in a large clear space and won't endanger anyone. You may already be able to skip stones over water.

Twig painting

Here's something else to try – painting with a twig. Aborigines chewed the end of a stick to make a paint brush, or tied fibres to it. Clays, the rich colours of the earth were used as paints. Browns, yellows, rusty-red and white.

Many of the paintings were abstract designs, sacred symbols with meaning to those who read and understood. They could be painted on bodies, bark, rock surfaces or scored in sand. Some told a story.

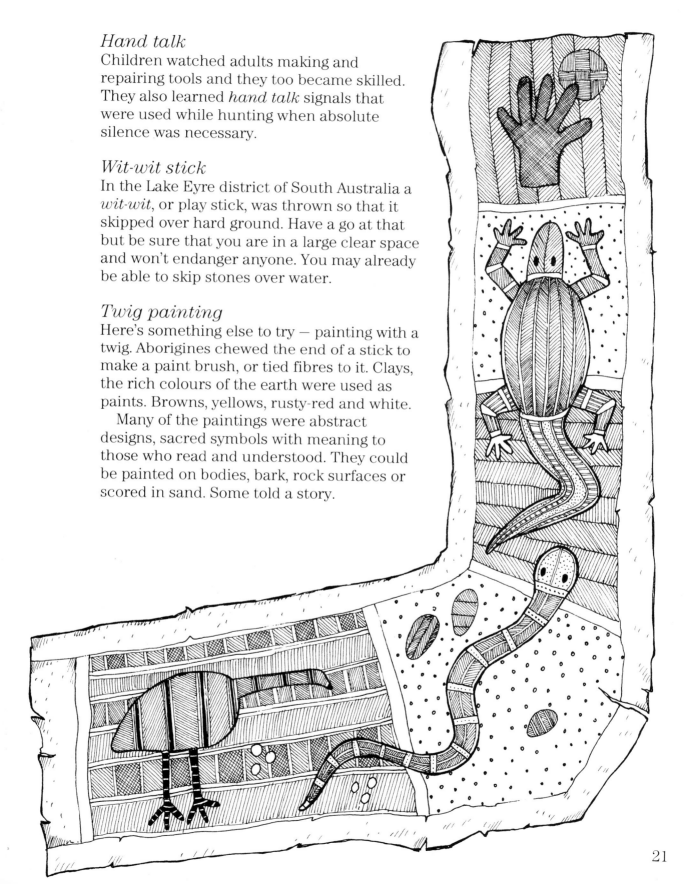

SLIDE DOWN THE SLOPE

Slide down the slope
of the sand ridge!
Laugh and cry out —
down to the bottom
and climb up the ridge.
Slide down again!

Children, like the one sliding down the sand dune, often spontaneously sang a song of their own. Others might pick up the rhythm and join in while playing . . .

tracking and hunting, running and jumping, climbing and diving, swimming and sliding or skidding in mud. *Eeeeeee!*

No child failed while learning a survival skill, although a few might progress more slowly than others. And so, there were songs for most things as well as play. Children sang about their land and the creatures who shared it with them.

TORTOISE

Long necked tortoise floats like paper bark
        flying in the water.
            Splash!
        She dives.

Small animals, especially lizards, made good dinner. Children, sharp-eyed and fleet-footed, were often quicker than a lizard, who ended up in a tucker bag. They knew how to track an animal, following almost invisible signs. They knew where the bees hid their hives and the secret places of honey ants and succulent witchetty grubs.

FRILLED-NECK LIZARD

I cling to the bark
half up a tree
and you don't see me.
I go round the tree
to the other side
As soon as your back is turned.

23

Where there was water, children soon knew the best places to dive for lily roots. Little girls owned a digging stick like the adults' and carried their own small dillybag to fill with the day's finds of roots, like yams.

MAKE A DILLYBAG

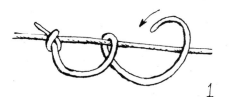

1

Aborigines often used hair to make twine. You can use heavy string. The amount you'll need will depend upon the size of the bag you want to make. The only other thing you need is patience.

   With one end of the string make a loop that is the size of the top of the bag you will make.

   Knot it off. Don't cut the string. Put the loop over a peg. A chair knob is ideal. Hold the loop out tightly in one hand. Remember this is the top of the bag.

   Now make knots along the loop as the picture shows. It's a good idea to leave plenty of room between the knots. Keep working until you've gone round the loop with knots.

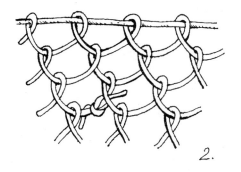

2.

   Now start the second row, working between the loops. Keep going and going, row after row. Work until you run out of string, or the bag is the length you want it to be.

   Tie off the string very securely.

   Sew up the bottom of the bag.
You can use differently coloured strings if you like.

3.

24

KOOBOO

In the Dreamtime there was this boy, Kooboo, who listened to no one and did as he pleased. Kooboo was troublesome and because he had no parents the tribe were patient with him.

Kooboo hid dillybags. He ran off with the women's digging sticks. He let the fire go out and played with the men's weapons. Kooboo wasted food and spilled water. Still, the people shared their food with him. But the time came when they could put up with him no longer. He was refused a meal.

The boy didn't care. He filled up on berries and leaves and to everyone's surprise he liked the taste of gum leaves. Kooboo didn't care if his people fed him, or not. He was as troublesome as ever.

For a long time Kooboo shared the water with his people. There was always a drink for Kooboo. Then the dry time came and everyone travelled a long way to waterholes. Kooboo didn't go walking for water. He cried and begged and squealed for the little that was carried back to the camp.

Eventually water became so scarce it was decided that Kooboo must walk for his own water. He decided to look for the spare water which the people had hidden in gourds, in some brush by a tall gum tree. Kooboo searched and searched until he found it. He drank and drank until he had quenched his thirst. Then he said, "I'll make sure that no one else gets the

rest of this water." So he took the gourds up the tree until he and the store of water were out of sight amongst the leaves. Kooboo waited. He waited.

The tribe returned at sunset and everyone was hot and badly in need of a drink. There was none in the hiding place in the scrub. Gourds and water were gone. And there were no tracks to show who had stolen the precious water. Kooboo's tracks were there, but Kooboo's tracks were everywhere about the camp. Still, they wondered where the boy was.

Before long someone glimpsed him, high in the tree. He sat comfortably on a branch cradling the gourds. "Come down at once," he was told.

Kooboo shrieked with laughter. "Come and get me," he taunted. "Here I am and here I stay. You didn't share the water so go off and find more if you want some."

He thought he was safe on his high perch. He was higher than anyone else could climb and at first nobody tried to reach him. Then, the smallest children began to whimper. Soon tongues felt swollen and mouths as dry as grit. Kooboo didn't care. He upended a gourd and guzzled noisily, letting water trickle wastefully down his chin and hands.

Two young men sprang at the tree trunk and climbed as high as they could. The tree top swayed. Kooboo was almost within their reach when something whacked sharply on their heads. Kooboo's jeering face warned them off. He had broken off a dried branch to prod them off the tree. They retreated before they fell.

Everyone was furious with Kooboo. Two more men tried to climb the tree. Again Kooboo waited until they were almost within arm's reach before hitting out with the branch. This time he broke the grip of one man. He fell, knocking against the second and both crashed to the ground. Kooboo's laughter, like the cackle of a bird, filled the evening and brought the Wise Man, the Clever One.

Before long Kooboo saw two more men climb the tree. He watched closely. The men didn't edge straight up as the others had done. They came swinging round the trunk. Round and round.

Koboo stopped laughing but he still looked pleased with himself as he broke off another branch. He threw it like a spear at the circling men and he missed. He threw a second and he missed. The men came on! Kooboo scrambled to the end of his bough, pulling off another dead branch as he went. He threw that. He missed again as the men circled under him. He began to sob. He begged for mercy but everyone had had enough of Kooboo and his pranks.

He was grabbed by the neck and pulled from his perch, then dropped to the ground, still grasping the gourds of water. They were wrenched from his grasp and the people rushed at him. Somehow he escaped.

No one attempted to chase. This wasn't their Kooboo, not irritating Kooboo who had annoyed them for so long. Something fur covered and smelling strongly of eucalyptus had fled from them. They drew back to watch a small animal lurch to the tree, then climb rapidly. When it was all but hidden behind puffballs of leaves it looked back over a shoulder and down at them. Round eyes glared, fringed ears twitched and a black nose sniffed. The animal looked down its pebble of a nose throwing them a look that reminded them of Kooboo. It was Kooboo!

He was a koala and for ever he lived in gum trees. For ever he ate leaves and rarely needed water. Kooboo never stole water again but he didn't stop moaning and crying about his fate either. He may still be at it to this day.

KOALA

The smudged track of koala
marks the grass
as he lurches past,
legs wide apart
but once in his tree ...
he climbs ... rapidly.

Tickle whistle

Hold a gum leaf very firmly against your mouth. Blow a tune
against it. Can you make it whistle and sing? Some people can.

Have you ever carefully stretched a gum leaf to see the pale
rubber-like substance under the green? Blow on it. What hap-
pens?

Crush some gum leaves and enjoy their smell. It's the smell
of the bush on a hot day.

BUNYIP HOLE

There was a lake where the people liked to go often. Its water was brackish, a little more salty than fresh. Ducks nested in the reeds but the lake was no longer a good camp. A bunyip had come to live in the darkest, murkiest, deepest part. The people heard his howls in the night and they knew that the bunyip was large and ferocious. Soon he killed some of the hunters by pulling swimmers' legs until they sank under the water, never to be seen again. Terror and anger upset the people. They needed their camp by the lake, with its flocks of water birds, so they refused to move to another place. They decided that the bunyip must go.

The people collected stones. Many, many stones. Piles of stones. The next day they attacked the bunyip, pelting the lake with the stones until the water boiled with froth and the birds flew away, squawking outrage. And along the shore, fires burned through the day until the air was thick with smoke, choking smoke. As well, the people screamed and shouted, making an ear-splitting uproar.

Bunyip felt the stones. Bunyip smelled the smoke. Bunyip heard the noise and dived even deeper into the dark, murky water. It did not move. Bunyip pretended he wasn't there, but the people knew better. They kept up their attack with more stones, more fires and more noise. Bunyip could find no place to hide away from it all.

When evening came, Bunyip was hungry. It could find no food. The birds had flown off and it liked bird for tucker. Some time between star-shine and moon-rise Bunyip rolled over and moaned, then poked its fearsome head cautiously from the water. It was no more than a peek. The smoke hurt its eyes and the noise hurt its ears. Bunyip roared and reared out of the water. It thrashed its tail again and again, drenching the land and the people and the fires, and the people saw the dark shape of it gliding away to the far end of the lake.

The bunyip didn't stop there. It crawled painfully up the bank, heaving itself from the water. Dragging its great belly over the ground, it headed south until it slipped thankfully into another waterhole. Coolness soothed its scraped hide. Sighing, the bunyip drank deeply, only to splutter and spit. The water was salt. There were no reeds here. No ducks. It howled, longing for the lake, or a muddy, swampy hole. It rolled its head and howled again.

The people didn't hear it. They sang and danced, sure that they had overcome the bunyip. Little did they know that it was returning. But the closer it came, the noisier were the people, and brighter and smokier were their fires. Bunyip's ears hurt. It moaned and clumsily turned to the west. West. West-ward! Westward it trundled searching for a fresh-

water creek or billabong and its disappointed howling spoiled the sleep of many. It may have found what it wanted, because the people stayed by the lake for a long time. They had bark shelters against the winds. They hunted ducks and other waterbirds who flew back in their flocks. They swam and fished while children played by the water. No one feared the bunyip any more. It never returned.

SLEEP TIME

To keep safe from bunyips, children slept in *gunyahs*. A *gunyah* is a simple shelter made from two forked sticks pushed into the ground. A third stick balanced between them to support a covering of leafy branches or bark.

In Western Australia some tribes built *wiltjas* which were more rounded in shape. The supporting frame was covered with spinifex or brush. A fire at the entrance kept off biting insects.

Caves also, were shelters from wind and rain. And in the summer, shelters were built on stilts above the mud.

It was sensible to keep out of the sun during the hottest part of the day and many families quickly built a screen from the sun or winds, or found shaded rocks where they could rest.

DINGO

Thirsty in the hot sun
His throat parched and dry,
He's gasping for breath.
His heart beats hard
As he stumbles towards
The shade of a tree
Where he can rest.

BILBA BANDICOOT

The biggest of all the bandicoots in the land was Bilba. She was three times taller and three times heavier than the rest, and when she dug it was like a sandstorm. Her broad, strong paws could dig through the hardest and driest of earth.

She lived with her tribe in a lonely valley where no one came because water and food were scarce. But Bilba could dig deeply for water. When it seeped into the hole she had made, there was enough for them all.

Early one evening, Bilba was dozing behind some rocks when the peace of the valley was broken by the harsh cries of hunting dingoes. Hungry, thirsty dogs, they had been driven from their place by drought. Their howls rose to a high pitch when they saw the bandicoots and they rushed in to attack.

Bilba rushed out from her rocks. She was closer to the dogs and her size confused them as she bounded up a slope. "Follow me!" barked Big Fella Dingo. "There's tucker for us all." And he followed Bilba along the ridge, with the other dogs streaming behind.

Even with her powerful legs it was hard for Bilba to keep ahead of the hungry dogs but she ran on, leading them further and further away from her tribe. Before long, she was far enough ahead to stop and dig frantically. Her paws flew. Dust flew, swirling in clouds and darkening the last of the day, while Bilba tunnelled deep into the earth.

"Quarry gone to earth!" howled Big Fella Dingo. "Dig her out."

The dingo mob milled about the mouth of the burrow as eager paws widened the entrance to break into her refuge. Bilba rushed out, leaping through the mob, thrusting bodies aside and somehow escaping snapping jaws. She fled up hill.

Snapping, barking, yelping dogs chased and almost caught her but little by little she drew ahead. Further ahead. Further. Once more she stopped. Once more she dug and her tunnel was deeper.

Soon the dingoes were digging above her head. Bilba could hear them and fear gave even more strength to her paws. Her position was hopeless. Their large number had beaten her. She would not be able to trick them again.

It was then that her paws felt damp and she scooped moist sand, then sand-mud. It quickly turned to slush oozing about her feet. Within moments she stood in water that sloshed as she moved and rose so quickly Bilba suddenly wondered if she would drown before the dingoes reached her.

The water swirled about her and Bilba panicked a little, kicking out with a foot. A stone dislodged under her and an enormous spout of water shot upwards with a tremendous gush that bored through the earth, taking Bilba with it.

Bilba was tossed aside as the escaping water spread outwards, pouring down the hillside. It bowled over dingoes, shook them, bashed them against rocks, swept them away and drowned a few. They struggled to keep afloat or tried to swim but they were washed downstream a long way. Some managed to scramble free and crying plaintively, they left the valley with their tails between their legs. It was a long time before they nosed about there again.

Bilba's digging had released a spring. It flowed over the dry earth to soak into it, then dribbled on through sand making billabong pools that never completely dried out during the hottest dry spells. So the bandicoots stayed there for a long time and danced many corroborees that told the story of Bilba and the dingoes.

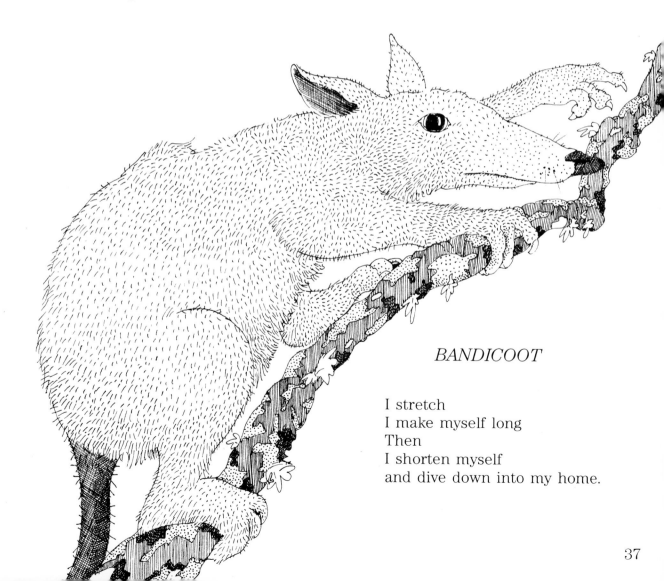

BANDICOOT

I stretch
I make myself long
Then
I shorten myself
and dive down into my home.

CORROBOREE

Corroboree may have been a word belonging to the Port Jackson people to describe a ceremony. Now it is in general use with a wider meaning that covers rituals or ceremonies, dancing and singing, or miming a story or an event.

Hot day dies, cook time comes.
Now between the sunset and sleeptime
Time to playabout.
The hunters paint black bodies by firelight with
     designs of meaning
To dance corroboree.
Now didgeridoo complete with haunting drone
     eager feet stamp
Click-sticks click in rhythm to swaying bodies
Dancing corroboree.
Like spirit things in from the great surrounding dark
Ghost-gums dimly seen stand at the edge of light
Watching corroboree.
Eerie the scene in leaping firelight,
Eerie the sounds in that wild setting,
As naked dancer weaves stories of the tribe
I to corroboree.

Kath Walker

BOHRAH KANGAROO

In the long-time of the Dreaming, darkness covered the land. Bohrah the Kangaroo did not like it, although he grazed at night. Bohrah liked the stars to shine and the moon to glow, so he rolled back the darkness as if it were a possum-skin rug and he left it there on the edge of the world.

Bohrah went on grazing under the stars and the moon, getting about on his four legs, just like the Dingo. One evening he looked up and saw camp fires in the distance, and he could hear voices singing. Being a curious fellow, he crept up to the fires and to his amazement saw strangely marked figures stepping out and about in the circle of firelight. They moved to the rhythm of clicking sticks and the thump-thump-thud of rolled possum rugs.

The beat quickened. The dancers' movements changed. Feet stamped fast, then faster. Voices chanted louder, then louder. And Bohrah watched until all died away to silence and he saw the dancers disappear into bush, away from the firelight.

Someone built up the fires and when the flames were brighter, the boomerangs clicked another rhythm and women's voices sang, as a long line of painted men emerged from the darkness to circle the fires. They danced and leapt, exciting Bohrah, who longed to join them. He stood up on his hind legs and balancing himself on his tail jumped into their midst.

The silence was as long as a drawn breath. Women broke it with shrieks of terror and Bohrah may have been killed instantly if he had not tried to dance. Someone tried to follow his rhythm with boomerang clicks. The possum-rug thumps joined in and so did the dancers who hopped after Bohrah, his long tail dragging in the dust. He held his forepaws in front of his chest and held his head upright as he circled gravely round and round.

Bohrah was so intent upon his steps that he failed to notice dancers slipping away into the darkness. They returned wearing tails of grass that trailed behind when they bounded after Bohrah, holding their hands as he did his paws.

Excitement increased. Then, the dance came to an abrupt end. An elder spoke, "This Bohrah has come to our camp. We did not invite him, and Bohrah danced when he should not have danced." Silence fell. The penalty was death for Bohrah, but soon people argued that Bohrah had shown them a new dance. Wasn't there another way to settle Bohrah's law breaking?

Eventually Bohrah was led away, taken to the initiation place, where he was made a member of the tribe. He left with some front teeth missing and the punishment of moving for ever on his strong hind legs. He still hops that way as you can see for yourself, and he still holds his forepaws neatly against his chest. That's Bohrah!

CAMP FIRE STARS

At one time the Kanula brothers fell in love with seven Makara sisters. They were tall and beautiful, with long hair, and their bodies were covered with icicles that sparkled brighter than diamonds. And although the brothers wooed the sisters with words and gifts of honey, the Makara remained shy and gently aloof, disappearing quickly when anyone came near.

This, however, was not enough protection against the Evil Man who came creeping into their camp one evening. He captured two of the girls. The others were able to escape. They fled upwards, springing into the sky, from where they gazed down and helplessly watched as their sisters were dragged to the Evil Man's camp.

He lit a fire to melt the icicles that hid the girls' beauty and pushed them towards its heat. The icicles dripped a little, dampening the fire until it all but went out. It hissed and smouldered and sent up smoke. The Evil One couldn't get it to burn again and he didn't want to eat raw meat — that was not to his liking. "Go and get some dry bark," he impatiently ordered the girls. "Take it from the pine tree by the creek. Feed that to the fire."

"We cannot touch a pine tree," the Makara warned him. He did not believe them. This was an excuse. "Do as you are told or I'll beat you both," he scowled, ugly with anger.

The Makara sisters ran to the creek and found the tree, knowing that the man's glaring eyes followed them. When they began to strip bark off the tree's trunk he seemed to be satisfied and turned away with a shrug. So he did not see the tree begin to grow, magically and he missed seeing the girls climb into its branches. But before long, he wondered why it took so long to return with the bark. His campfire was almost out. He was hungry. He wanted to eat — cooked food.

The Evil Man strode towards the creek and at first, he couldn't see the pine tree. He was looking too low. Then, his eyes lifted and he was astonished. It was growing taller and taller. On the topmost branches perched the two beautiful Makara maidens. "Come down at once!" he shouted. They ignored his cries, and his threats. He shook the tree trunk. Its top swayed dangerously. The girls clung to their branch and the tree pierced through clouds until it tipped the sky. Helpful hands pulled the Makara out of the branches and they were reunited with their five sisters. Their rejoicing was great, but, below them, on the land the Kanula brothers grieved when they heard of their loss. They grieved until their hearts broke and the brothers died.

The Great Spirits heard of their death and were moved by the brothers' love for the Makara. And so, they took them up to the heavens.

Each day the men hunted for game and the wild bees' nests while the seven sisters gathered grass seeds, roots and fruit. After they had eaten, the Kanulas and the Makara sisters sang and danced. On a cloudless night, if you look, you'll see their camp fires. The brothers have become the beautiful constellation of Orion and the Makara sisters shine as the seven stars of the group called Pleiades, but two don't sparkle as brilliantly as the others. The Evil Man melted some of their brilliance with his camp fire, but on the coldest winter days all of the girls shake frost from their bodies. It falls as snow in the highlands, putting out unsheltered fires. At other times the sisters send down rain, when they jump noisily into their waterhole until it overflows, pouring down on the land. You can hear them in the thunder but you won't see them, except at night, when back in the sky they gleam, not far from Orion.

EVENING STAR

Up and up soars the Evening Star
hanging there in the sky.
Men watch it, at the Place of the Dugong,
the Place of the Clouds,
the Place of the Evening Star.
Far off, at the Place of the Mist,
the Place of the Lilies,
the Place of the Dugong,
The Lotus, Evening Star hangs there,
on its long stalk
held by the Spirits.

In the far North the waterlily is the symbol of a star. Its flower
is star light. The stalk is the path nightly followed by the star
crossing the sky.

SKY CHART

Aboriginal children could read the skies for the changing
seasons. Stars and the sun were used like a map or chart, as
well as calendar and clock. Can you tell what time of day it is
by the position of the sun? Test yourself. Can you tell the
direction north from the sun's position?

Have you noticed how the stars shift positions in the sky?
Where is the Southern Cross in the summer?

By the time an Aboriginal child was about twelve years old
much would have been learned about the tribe's way of life,
the land and its creatures, as well as the sky. The carefree
days of childhood would soon end with initiation rites that
made both girls and boys full members of their tribe and
responsible people.

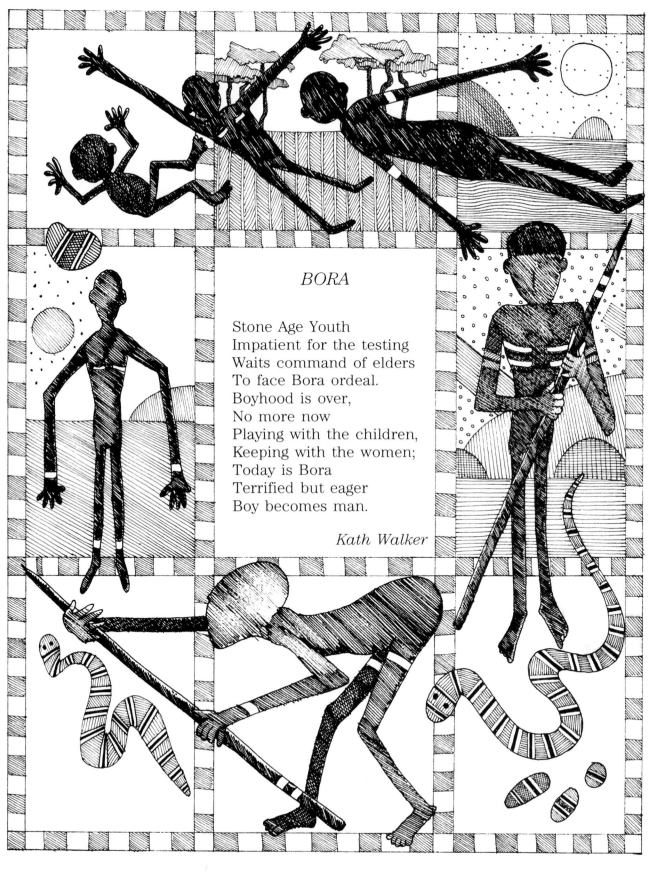

BORA

Stone Age Youth
Impatient for the testing
Waits command of elders
To face Bora ordeal.
Boyhood is over,
No more now
Playing with the children,
Keeping with the women;
Today is Bora
Terrified but eager
Boy becomes man.

Kath Walker

CHANGE

The coming of the first Europeans to live on the East Coast of Australia changed life for most Aborigines. It happened slowly, ending a way of living that had evolved over thousands of years.

The Aborigines did not own land in the European sense. The land owned them.

It was a long time before others began to understand.

BOTANY BAY

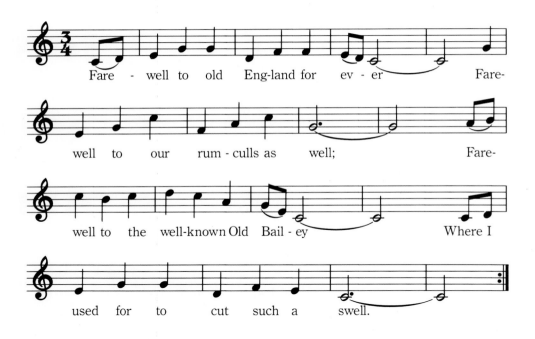

Chorus
Singing too-ra-lie, too-ra-lie, addity,
Singing too-ra-lie, too-ra-lie, aye,
Singing too-ra-lie, too-ra-lie, addity,
We're bound for Botany Bay.

T'aint leaving Old England we cares about,
    T'aint 'cause we mis-spells what we knows;
But because all we light-fingered gentry
    Hops around with a log on our toes.

There's the captain as is our commander,
    There's the bosun and all the ship's crew,
There's the first and second class passengers
    Knows what we poor convicts goes through.

For fourteen long years I'm transported,
    For fourteen long years and a day,
Just for meeting a cove in the alley,
    And stealing his ticker away.

Oh, had I the wings of a turtle-dove!
    I'd soar on my pinions so high;
Slap bang to the arms of my Polly-love
    And in her sweet bosom I'd die.

Now all you young dukies and duchesses,
    Take warning from what I do say,
Mind, all is your own as you touchesses,
    Or you'll meet us in Botany Bay.

SETTLEMENT

In May, 1787, eleven small ships left Portsmouth in England, bound for Botany Bay. It took eight months and one day to reach New Holland, and then the fleet didn't stay at Botany Bay. They upped anchor and sailed along the coast a little further into Port Jackson. It looked to be a very fine harbour. And it was — one of the best. So, on a sultry January day in 1788, the city of Sydney had its beginnings as a convict settlement.

Convicts came on the ships. Marines came on the ships. Forty-one children came on the ships.

BOBBY SHAFTO

Bobby Shafto's gone to sea,
Silver buckles on his knee,
He'll come back and marry me,
Bonny Bobby Shafto!

Possibly none of the boys with the fleet wore silver buckles at the knees, although a few may have had shoe buckles like the adults'. Children's clothing then was similar to the grown-ups, even to frilled shirt collars for the boys. Mary Ann, the daughter of Marine Wright, who sailed with her parents on the *Prince of Wales*, had ankle length skirts like her mamma's. A mob cap or a bonnet would have covered her long hair. Perhaps it was fair like Bobby's.

Bobby Shafto's fat and fair,
Combing down his yellow hair.
He's my love forever more,
Bonny Bobby Shafto!

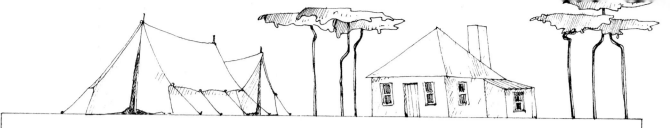

Henrietta and Philip Langley were passengers on the *Lady Penrhyn*. They may never have made a return voyage. Their father was a convict. However, John White who sailed on the *Alexander* as a ship's boy possibly returned to England, little knowing the hard struggle ahead for the settlement.

For several years food was desperately short and severely rationed. The seasons seemed to be turned upside down and the early crops failed. At first, people lived in tents while crude huts were built along the Tank Stream. The walls were wattle and daub. The floors were dirt. The roofs, thatched with reeds, caught fire so often that it became a safety habit to build kitchens apart from the main house. This was continued for many years.

Soon the tent village became a shanty town. The shanty town gave way to more permanent houses and solid buildings and those houses and farms took land that had been Aboriginal hunting grounds. Slowly the Aborigines realized that their visitors had come to stay.

FIRST BORN

No one can positively identify the very first European child to be born in Australia. Some claim that she was Diana Kable. Others are sure that it was a little girl called Rebecca West, but her birthday was in September, 1788.

Between January and July of that same year there were seven babies baptised, with little James Thomas as first on the records kept by St Philip's Church. It is not recorded if the children were born in England, on the ships, or in the colony.

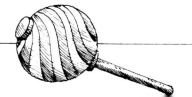

BABY BUNTING

Lullaby, Baby Bunting,
Your father's gone a-hunting,
To catch a rabbit for the skin,
To wrap a Baby Bunting in.

The old nursery rhyme would have come with the memories of the early settlers. Memories took up no space on the little ships whose cargoes were barely enough to start the colony. However, people did remember stories as well as rhymes to tell the children. This is how I like to tell one of them, although Tom Thumb had many adventures.

TOM THUMBE

In the time when the world was a better place than it is now, a ploughman made a wish aloud. He wished for a son. "Even if he's no bigger than my thumb, I'd be glad of him," said the man. The Queen of the Fairies happened to overhear his very words, so she saw to it that his wish was granted. And when a son was born to the ploughman's wife he was no bigger than a thumb! The child grew no taller either, nor stronger, or older — not after he was four minutes old! So, what did they call him? Tom Thumbe, just as you would expect.

The Queen of the Fairies was his godmother and she decked him out in clothes of her own making. His shirt was woven from cobwebs and his coat was woven from thistledown. He wore an oak leaf hat that had a feather from a titmouse and on his legs were stockings, cunningly woven from the skin of a green apple. They were held up by garters made from two hairs from his mother's head. And shoes? Yes, he had shoes. One mousie's skin provided enough leather for twelve pairs of shoes and slippers to boot.

Tom Thumbe was a proper little gallant when he sallied forth but he had to be careful that the wind didn't blow him away down the street when he went to play with the neighbours' children. He liked to play Pins and Points. That was a game with the metal tags used to fasten children's clothes before buttons and other fasteners were invented. In another game the children used cherry stones that they kept in little bags. Pins were part of yet another game and these were stored in little boxes. Tom Thumbe, being hardly old at all, knew nothing about the rules of the games and would help himself to others' cherry stones, or help himself to someone's pin-box. He even foraged in the children's pockets.

Before long he infuriated one lad who grabbed hold of Tom Thumbe and pushed him into a pin-box, then slid the lid shut. That may have been the end of Tom Thumbe, wasting away in the dark without any food, but, the Queen of the Fairies had given Tom the gift of invisibility. Soon, the lad was opening the box to peek at his captive and away Tom flitted, seeking revenge.

How could such a little fellow do that? Well, first of all he hung his mother's pots and pans, cups and glasses on a sunbeam. As straight as an arrow the sunbeam shone through the window. Glasses glinted, cups sparkled and pans shone. It all delighted the children who ran home to do the same with their mothers' belongings. Crash! Crash! Crash! Down fell glasses and cups! Down tumbled pots and pans. Oh! Oh! yelled the children holding on to their slapped bottoms. And mothers warned,

"If thou wilt from whipping
keepe safely thy bum,
Take heed of the pastimes,
here taught by Tom Thumbe."

Tom Thumbe crowed with delight to hear all this
and swaggered into his mother's kitchen where she
was making a pudding.

It was dark in the kitchen because it was a dull
day, and to see better what his mother was doing,
Tom climbed on the table and then to the edge of the
mixing bowl. There he balanced, holding a candle
above his head so his mother could work in its light.
Round went the spoon round the bowl ... round ...
round ... round. Watching it made Tom feel sleepy.
He closed his eyes. He lost his balance and fell into
the bowl.

Eeek! His mam screeched. She fished the candle
from the bowl and search as she would she did not
find Tom Thumbe. However, she was blinded by tears
and didn't see him crawl like a fly from the batter
that covered him from head to foot. Wailing with
grief, she absent-mindedly picked him up in her
thumb and forefinger as if he were a currant or a
spot of stray fat, and dropped Tom Thumbe back in
the bowl.

Before he could surface the pudding was in its
cloth, tied with a knot and plopped into a pot of
scalding water.

Tom was in the middle of the pudding but kicking
and pushing he worked his way towards the edge,
before he was smothered by batter. The pot rocked
and rumbled, then bounced. "It's bewitched!"

screamed Tom's mam just as there was a knock on the door and a voice cried, "I'm a hungry tinker, Mistress. Can you give me a bite to eat?"

She gave him the pot with its bouncing pudding and he ran off with it before she changed her mind. He ran and he ran until he reached a tree where he sat himself down with the pudding pot that still rumbled and bounced. "It's the devil in there!" yelped the tinker. And he was off, wild-eyed and gasping. Over the fence and away.

The pot fell over. The pudding rolled out and by and by Tom struggled free. He had eaten his way to daylight and still had the strength to scramble out of the cloth, then struggle all the way home to his mam. She was very pleased to see him, and for ever after she called any pudding of such roundness and thickness, a *Tom Thumbe*, although he was never shut inside one again. Still, he had other adventures and you may meet him again.

FINGER COUNT

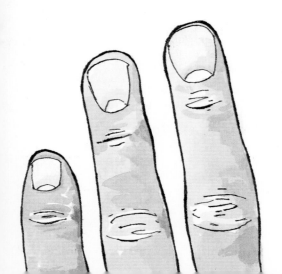

Thumb bold,
Thibity-thold,
Langman,
Lick pan,
Mammie's wee man.

Even today, anything very small might be called Tom Thumb.

Tom Thumb was the name of a tiny boat that sailed off to explore the south coast of New South Wales. It carried a seaman, a doctor and a boy. We don't know the boy's name but the seaman was Matthew Flinders and the doctor, George Bass.

LITTLE "TOM THUMB"

From Botany Bay
they all set sail,
a doctor and a sailor
and a boy to bail.
Out through the Heads
and sailing south
little "Tom Thumb"
left the harbour mouth.
"Tom Thumb" pitched,
"Tom Thumb" rolled,
the sea-wind blew
and they all got cold;
they all got wet
with flying spray
as little "Tom Thumb"
sailed south-away.

They came to a beach
and stepped ashore.
The boy didn't have
to bail any more.
They dried their clothes
and made new friends
where the south coast starts
and the east coast ends.
Then back to sea
and sailing home,
safe to Sydney,
wet with foam —
A boy to bail,
a doctor and his chum,
not forgetting
little "Tom Thumb".

W. N. Scott

55

Some years later Matthew Flinders sailed round Tasmania and proved that it was an island. Then, off he went again, completely round Australia itself. All the way he made charts and some are still used today. Matthew had a cat called Trim. And Matthew named this country Australia. Previously, people had called it New Holland, or Terra Australis, the Great South Land.

The bailer boy on board Matthew's *Tom Thumb* was more than likely born in England. Strange as it may seem, the colony was a better place for him to be. Children in England were poorly treated, often cruelly. Many were drudges from the age of six, or younger. They worked long hours in coal mines, mills and factories, or as underpaid servants, or chimney sweeps. Shamefully, children were sometimes sold by uncaring or desperately poor parents.

THE CHIMNEY SWEEPER

When my mother died I was very young
And my father sold me while yet my tongue
Could scarcely cry, 'Weep! weep! weep! weep!'
So your chimneys I sweep and in soot I sleep.

The new colony had no factories where children were beaten awake or for making mistakes. Convicts provided free labour. And when farms were hacked out of the bush a child then might work for his family, helping to clear timber, ploughing, chopping wood and carrying water. Girls helped with pigs and poultry and the milking of cows. And there was butter to make, bread to make, cheese to make, clothes to make! And the washing had to be done, sticks gathered for the fire and smaller children to be minded. Still, the sun mostly shone and there was time to play.

No one bothered boys with too many baths and it was off to bed by lamp or candle light — candles made by mother. The colony's children grew straight-limbed and healthy, despite the times when pantries were as empty as Old Mother Hubbard's.

OLD MOTHER HUBBARD

Old Mother Hubbard
Went to the cupboard
To give the poor dog a bone;
When she came there,
The cupboard was bare,
And so the poor dog had none.

She went to the baker's
To buy him some bread;
When she came back
She thought he was dead!

She went to the undertaker's
To buy him a coffin;
When she came back
The dog was laughing.

She took a clean dish
To get him some tripe;
When she came back
He was smoking a pipe.

She went to the alehouse
To get him some beer;
When she came back
The dog sat in a chair.

She went to the tavern
   For white wine and red;
When she came back
   The dog stood on his head.

She went to the fruiterer's
   To buy him some fruit;
When she came back
   He was playing the flute.

She went to the tailor's
   To buy him a coat;
When she came back
   He was riding a goat.

She went to the hatter's
   To buy him a hat;
When she came back
   He was feeding her cat.

She went to the barber's
   To buy him a wig;
When she came back
   He was dancing a jig.

She went to the cobbler's
To buy him some shoes;
When she came back
He was reading the news.

She went to the seamstress
To buy him some linen;
When she came back
The dog was spinning.

She went to the hosier's
To buy him some hose;
When she came back
He was dressed in his clothes.

The Dame made a curtsy,
The dog made a bow;
The Dame said, 'Your servant'.
The dog said, 'Bow-wow'.

This wonderful dog
He was Dame Hubbard's delight,
He could read, he could dance,
He could sing, he could write;
She gave him rich dainties
Whenever he fed,
And erected a monument
When he was dead.

KEEPING CLEAN

Although colonial children were healthier than the children living in cramped, colder England, many, many monuments were raised to little children who died during the 19th century. Families were often large. Immunization against child killing diseases was yet to be discovered. Anaesthetics were still experimental. Little was known about the spread of disease through close contact with others, flies and contaminated foods. Hygiene was difficult. There were no sewers, poor drainage and no refrigeration. Water was collected from streams, wells or tanks.

It took effort to be sweet and clean. Someone lugged the hot water for baths from a copper to a laundry tub placed in front of a kitchen fire. Or, it was carried to a bedroom and poured into a hip bath. A very uncomfortable thing! Look out for one in a folk museum. Several people were likely to bath in the same water, maybe once each week! Small children were 'topped and tailed' at bedtime, with a quick scrub of faces, hands and feet. No one had bathrooms. A rag dipped in salt cleaned teeth, if they were cleaned at all. Tooth decay was achingly high.

OLD WOMAN FROM LEITH

There was an old woman from Leith,
Who had a sad pain in her teeth;
But the blacksmith uncouth
Scared the pain from her tooth
Which rejoiced the old woman from Leith.

TWO PENNIES FOR SCHOOL

Two convicts began the first school when the settlement was just one year old. The classes were held on six days during a week and it cost two pennies for each child to attend. That was more costly than marines and convicts could afford, so some children only went to school occasionally, or not at all. And so, there were children who didn't learn to read or write.

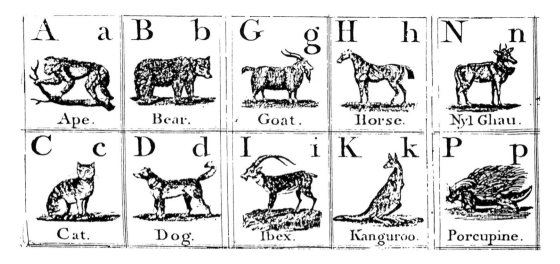

WRITING WITH A FEATHER

As more convicts and then settlers came to the colony, private schools were opened for the children of the well-to-do. As well as reading, writing and arithmetic, these children were also taught morals, manners and deportment. They wrote with stiff quills made from goose feathers, dipping them into ink pots and staining fingers. And slate pencils scratched and scraped over slates while the youngest learned their alphabet from a *battledore*. It was shaped like a washer woman's paddle at one time, then in stiff paper that could be folded into three. This one from 1794, possibly was the very first to mention an Australian animal. You'll soon spot that but you would spell the name differently.

WHITE MAN'S SCHOOL

Aboriginal children whose tribal land spread out from Port Jackson, had become refugees in their own country as the settlement widened. They were offered schooling of a kind. It included training as stockmen or rouseabouts, nursemaids or housemaids for the colony. Payment was often food and clothing, and the food was inferior to that available in the bush. Sugar, flour and rum were poor substitutes. Not many children went to the white man's school.

FEAR THE ROD

Elizabeth Macarthur didn't either. Her father had sheep and he could afford a governess for his little girls. However, his sons, Edward, James, John and William took the long voyage to England to attend school where no doubt, they learned Latin and Greek and were severely disciplined. '*Let the child from one year old to fear the rod, and to cry softly if you whip him ten times running to effect it,*' was the opinion of one man of this time. Hopefully, most adults were kinder to children.

ELIDOR

In the days when Henry I was King of England and that's a goodly time long past, there was a little lad called Elidor who was being brought up to become a monk. Day after day he trudged from his mother's house up to the Scriptorium where the monks did their writing and he learnt his alphabet, then to read and to write.

Alas, Elidor was a lazy little rogue. As fast as he learnt one letter he forgot another, so it was little progress that he made. The good monks shook their heads, then remembered the saying, 'Spare the rod and spoil the child', so they gave him a few whacks to help him remember. At first the rod was used lightly and sparingly but Elidor was not a boy to be driven. Soon there were more and more beatings and the more he was whacked the less Elidor learned. In the end he could stand it no longer and upped and fled into the great forest of St. David.

Elidor, who was about twelve years old and without fear, wandered about for two days and two nights. He had nothing to eat but rose hips, but he was determined not to return to the Scriptorium, the monks and a beating. So, he was not only hungry but exhausted when he came upon a cave. Thankfully he went into it, sinking down on its earthy floor to rest.

All at once, two little people stood before him. "Come with us," they ordered Elidor. "We'll lead you to the land of food, games and sports."

Food! Elidor couldn't resist the invitation and he followed them down a passage at the back of the cave. It went under the ground into darkness, winding through the earth, on and on. Suddenly, there was a very sharp bend and Elidor stepped out into a pleasant place of rivers and plains, woodland and hills. Curiously, Elidor noticed at once, there was no sun. It didn't bother him because straight away he was introduced to a king. "You'll take care of my son." decreed the king after inspecting Elidor.

The prince was much smaller than Elidor. He hardly came to Elidor's waist. The rest of the Little People were no taller, yet they were built in proportion to their short height. Their heads, bodies, arms and legs were the exact size for them, and all small heads were covered in long fair hair that fell straight to their little narrow shoulders. They seemed to eat nothing at all, just drinking modestly a kind of milk that was flavoured with saffron. Yellow milk!

Not only was their diet strange and inadequate for Elidor he also missed the sun, the moon, the stars and the clouds. He missed his mother, too, and longed to see someone of his own height. Eventually he begged permission from the king to visit his mother. "She will be wondering where I've been all these days," he explained.

And so she had. "Where have you been?" she cried. "What have you done?" she shouted. When she heard about his adventure she pleaded with Elidor to stay with her, but he had promised the king that he would return to the Land of the Little People.

Elidor, then, spent some time with the little prince and some with his mother, who had no one else in all the world but her Elidor. One day he mentioned to her that the children of the Little People played with golden balls. "They'd be real gold. True gold!" she told Elidor with her eyes round with awe. "Just one little ball would give us plenty for the rest of our lives," she sighed. Her remark often flitted about Elidor's head and soon he had a chance to grab up a golden plaything, then rush through the underground passage towards home.

Angry men followed. He heard shouts and yells, indignant screams and running feet. Elidor ran until his breath left him, but somehow he managed to run on, to dart out of the passage into sunlight. He lurched through the forest clutching the ball. Behind him streamed the Little People, shouting and waving their fists and fuming such anger that Elidor was afraid.

He stumbled through the door of his mother's one roomed cottage, bleating, "Mother!" He fell at her feet. The ball flew out of his hand. She bent to pick it up as Little People surged about her, gibbering, snarling and spitting, pinching and pulling horrible faces. Then they were gone, and so was the golden ball.

When Elidor dared to venture into the silent forest again he could not find the cave, although he searched diligently. "You never will find it," his mother told him. "All that spitting and snarling was a hiding spell. No one will find the Little People again, Elidor."

She may have been right. So, Elidor went back to the Scriptorium and to the monks' surprise he became a better scholar. He learnt Latin and Greek and other things without too many whacks, and he arrived in good time for his lessons.

A DILLER, A DOLLAR

A diller, a dollar,
A ten o'clock scholar,
What makes you come so soon?
You used to come at ten o'clock
But now you come at noon.

TWO HOURS FOR DINNER AND PLAY

There were so many children in Sydney Town when the colony was thirteen years old that an Orphan School was established at Parramatta. There many little boys were supposed to have learnt to swear, drink and smoke! However, we know from records that the children were out of bed, dressed and working in the garden before breakfast at 8 o'clock.

Then came lessons, from 9 to 12. Then followed two hours for dinner and play. During the afternoons the boys were taught skills like blacksmithing, or shoe making, tailoring or carpentry. The girls learnt spinning, laundering and sewing.

ARE YOU GOING TO SCARBOROUGH FAIR?

Traditional

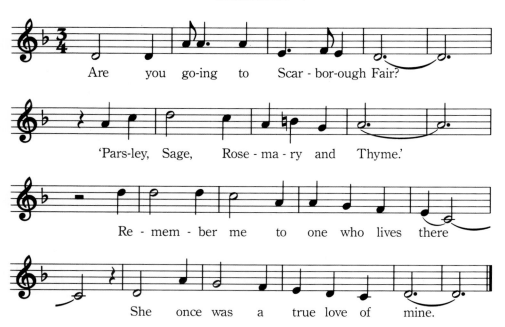

Are you go-ing to Scar-bor-ough Fair?

'Pars-ley, Sage, Rose-ma-ry and Thyme.'

Re-mem-ber me to one who lives there

She once was a true love of mine.

Tell her to make me a cambric shirt.
Parsley, Sage, Rosemary and Thyme.
Without no seam, nor needlework.
Then she'll be a true love of mine.

SEW A FINE SEAM

A shirt made without seam or needlework! Without any sewing at all. That sounds difficult! Little girls learnt a variety of
stitches by making *samplers*, doing beautiful work when as
young as eight years old. There were no sewing machines for
fast seaming. Clothes were hand stitched. The first sewing
machines were later worked manually by turning a little wheel
that resulted in chain-stitching. It came undone too easily and
sometimes disastrously.

PUT YOUR PLAYTHINGS AWAY

Haste! put your playthings all away,
Tomorrow is the Sabbath-day;
Come! bring me your Noah's ark,
Your pretty tinkling music-cart,
Because my love, you must not play,
But holy keep the Sabbath-day.

In 1819, long before that verse was written, two girls, Elizabeth and Ann, started up a Sunday School at Parramatta. They were the daughters of the clergyman, Samuel Marsden and they gathered together nineteen children, including some Aboriginal boys and girls. They would have recited the following prayer, which was written around 1795.

I will praise God with
my voice; for *I* may
praise *H*im, though I
am but a child. *A* few
years past, my tongue
was dumb in my mouth;
and *I* did not know the
great name of *God. B*ut
now *I* can speak, and
my tongue shall praise
*H*im; *I* can think of all
*H*is works, and my heart
shall love *H*im.

A MOTHER'S OFFERING

The first children's book published in Australia was written as settlement expanded as far as Western Australia and South Australia. Large grants of land were given out by the government, and those who failed to receive land often pushed further afield to *squat* — to take up land without anyone's consent. Aborigines retaliated, their spears ineffective against guns and sometimes Europeans shamefully poisoned water-holes. The tragic ignorance of another race of people encouraged a superior attitude amongst European Australians. This is evident in our first book. *A mother's offering to her children* was written by an unnamed "Lady long resident in New South Wales". She also offered some very peculiar information about the colony so who could she have been? She dedicated the book to the little son of Governor Darling so it's suspected that the author was his governess.

Here's a little from the book, but you need to know first, that in 1834 some survivors from a shipwreck in Torres Strait were murdered by natives, except for two boys and a baby. The *Tigris*, a brig left Sydney to rescue the children but another ship reached them earlier. We pick up the story where the captain has invited some of the islanders to his ship. Four children question the author who calls herself Mrs Saville.

ISLAND ENCOUNTER

Mrs Saville: There were women among them, who came on board without hesitation. They were not remarkable for their youth nor beauty. Being without clothing, the officers undertook to dress out one, and the boatswain another.

Emma: Had they women's clothes, Mamma?

Mrs Saville:	They had nothing but male attire; but the ladies were not fastidious. The old lady the boatswain had undertaken to adorn was unfortunately somewhat stout, and being encumbered with a huge bunch of strong coarse grass, there was difficulty in getting her into the dress; she could not be prevailed on to part with the grass, so the boatswain was obliged to pipe for more hands, and by dint of squeezing and shaking, she was fairly crushed into the trousers, which not being intended, as the boatswain said, to carry such stowage had a most ridiculous effect.
Julius:	Ha! Ha! Ha! How I should have laughed to have seen the horrid old creature.
Mrs Saville:	I have no doubt of it; you appear pretty well amused even at this distance of time and place.
Julius:	Yes, Mamma, and Lucy looks so grave, it makes me laugh more.
Lucy:	Yes, Julius, because I cannot laugh at such naughty bad people.
Julius:	Only conceive, Lucy, an old fat creature, like one of our old black women, stuffed into a tight pair of trousers. That would make a judge laugh.
Clara:	How did they manage with the other lady, Mamma?
Mrs Saville:	The dressing did not prove so difficult a task, she was neither so stout, nor so determined to retain her equipment of grass. It was therefore thrown aside, and she was not a little proud of her new dress; to which was added a Union Jack for a head-dress.

Lucy:	Dear! how gay she must have looked. I suppose this would make them all wish to have a *turban.
Mrs Saville:	They could not spare any more. This was an old boat's colour, belonging to one of the officers. The natives were very anxious for the Captain to go on shore. After breakfast he accepted their invitation, and went loaded with presents, instead of firearms.
Clara:	I should not like to trust any savages, Mamma, they are so treacherous. Poor Captain Cook, and many others, have felt the consequences of putting faith in unprincipled savages.
Mrs Saville:	Very true; I think it was imprudent. However, the Captain, surgeon, and mates went; the Purser and Second Lieutenant taking passage in one of their canoes directly afterwards. The Captain walked away arm in arm with the blacks (upon landing) to a hut and began to distribute his gifts. The women were most extravagant in wanting everything they saw, and very difficult to satisfy.
Lucy:	How greedy!
Mrs Saville:	They would attempt to snatch, and then the Captain closed up the canvas bag which held the treasures till silence and order was restored, when he began again. At last they became so vociferous, and crowded the Captain so much, in their eagerness to grasp the things, that he was almost suffocated. Some old women in particular, actually screeching in their anxiety to be heard above the rest, so that he hastily emptied the contents of his bag.

Emma:	Did they give the Captain anything in return, Mamma?
Mrs Saville:	Some took off their necklaces and offered them to him, but he made them to understand by signs that he did not want anything in return.
Julius:	What did his gifts consist of, Mamma?
Mrs Saville:	Of axes, knives, fishing-hooks, spikes and small nails, for the men; glass beads, small looking-glasses, scissors and handkerchiefs for the women. He also gave the men some cigars and † lucifer boxes.
Julius:	I dare say they were delighted with them.
Mrs Saville:	They were so stupid that the Captain could not make them understand how to get a light; and they teased him sadly, by their childish plaguing, to have their cigars lighted by him.
Julius:	Did they like the cigars, Mamma?
Mrs Saville:	Yes, they appeared to relish them very much, after smoking part of his, one stuck it through the cartilage of his nose.

* *turbans* were a popular head-dress then worn by women.
† *lucifer boxes* were matches.

WHITE MAN GOT NO DREAMING

White man got no dreaming,
Him go 'nother way.
White man, he go different.
Him go road belong himself.

Most books came from Britain. The better ones for children were decorated with gold leaf, with hand coloured illustrations neatly painted by small children who often worked in poor light and cramped conditions for very little. Translations of the Grimm stories were shipped to the colony. Here's a favourite.

RUMPEL-STILTS-KIN

In a certain kingdom once lived a poor miller who had a very beautiful daughter. She was moreover exceedingly shrewd and clever. The miller was so vain and proud of her, that he one day told the king of the land that his daughter could spin gold out of straw. Now this king was exceedingly fond of money and when he heard the miller's boast, his avarice was excited. He ordered the girl to be brought before him. Then he led her to a chamber where there was a great quantity of straw, gave her a spinning-wheel, and said, "All this must be spun into gold before morning, as you value your life". It was in vain that the poor maiden declared that she could do no such thing. The chamber was locked and she remained alone.

She sat down in one corner of the room and began to lament over her hard fate, when on a sudden the door opened, and a droll-looking little man hobbled in, and said, "Good morning to you, my good lass, what are you weeping for?"

"Alas!" answered she. "I must spin this straw into gold, and I know not how."

"What will you give me?" said the little man. "What will you give me to do it for you?"

"My necklace," replied the maiden. He took her at her word, and set himself down to the wheel. Round it went merrily, and presently the work was done and the gold all spun.

When the king came and saw this, he was greatly astonished and pleased but his heart grew still more greedy of gain. He shut up the poor miller's daughter again with a fresh task. Then she knew not what to do and sat down once more to weep. The little man presently opened the door, and said, "What will you give me to do your task?"

"The ring on my finger," replied she. So her little friend took the ring, and began to work at the wheel, till by the morning all was finished again.

The king was vastly delighted to see all this glittering treasure. Still he was not satisfied, and he took the miller's daughter into a yet larger room, and said, "All this must be spun tonight. If you succeed, you shall be my queen."

As soon as she was alone the dwarf came in, and said, "What will you give me to spin gold for you this third time?"

"I have nothing left," said she.

"Then promise me," said the little man, "your first little child when you are queen".

"That may never be," thought the miller's daughter. But as she knew no other way to get her task done, she promised him what he asked, and he spun once more the whole heap of gold.

The king came in the morning, and finding all he wanted, married her, and so the miller's daughter became queen.

At the birth of her first child the queen rejoiced very much, and forgot the little man and her promise. But one day he came into her chamber and reminded her of it. Then she grieved sorely at her misfortune, and offered him all the treasures of the kingdom in exchange but in vain. At last her tears softened him, and he said, "I will give you three days' grace, and if during that time you tell me my name, you shall keep your child."

Now the queen lay awake all night, thinking of all the odd names that she had ever heard, and dispatched messengers all over the land to enquire after new ones. The next day the little man came, and she began with Timothy, Benjamin, Jeremiah, and all the names she could remember. To all of them he said, "That's not my name".

The second day she began with all the comical names she had heard of, Bandy-legs, Hunch-back, Crook-shanks, and so on. The little gentleman still said to every one of them, "That's not my name".

The third day one of the messengers came back and said, "I have heard of no other name. But yesterday, as I was climbing a high hill among the trees of the forest where the fox and hare bid each other goodnight, I saw a little hut, and before the hut burnt a fire, and round the fire danced a funny little man upon one leg. He sang a song:

Merrily the feast I'll make,
Tomorrow I'll brew, tomorrow bake.
Merrily I'll dance and sing,
For the next day will a stranger bring.
Little does my lady dream
Rumpel-Stilts-Kin is my name."

When the queen heard this, she jumped for joy. So as soon as her little visitor came, and said, "Now, Lady, what is my name?"

"Is it John?" asked she.

"No!"

"Is it Tom?"

"No!"

"Can your name be *Rumpel-Stilts-Kin?*"

"Some witch told you that! Some witch told you that!" cried the little man and dashed his right foot in a rage so deep into the floor, that he was forced to lay hold of it with both hands to pull it out. Then he made the best of his way off, while everybody laughed at him for having had all his trouble for nothing.

HURT NO LIVING THING

Hurt no living thing
Ladybird or butterfly,
Nor moth with dusty wing,
Nor cricket chirping cheerfully,
Nor dancing gnat, nor beetle fat,
Nor harmless worms that creep.

Christina Rossetti 1879

CHAPBOOKS

As well as expensive books there were cheap, tiny ones that children so treasured they were usually worn to tatters. Most educated adults loathed them, preferring catechisms and religious texts. No chapbooks for their children! The chapbooks had been hawked up and down Britain for about a century past by the pedlars — the chapmen. They carried them in their packs with small household requirements, from market to market, from cottage door to cottage door and the children loved them. The chapbooks were printed on the poorest of paper, often just a folded page. They were full of spelling errors and misused grammar and crude wood-cuts, but they often told the old traditional stories. Without doubt, the children themselves imported them into Australia, by slipping them into a pocket, then reading and rereading, even swapping chapbooks for another story, maybe even *The Butterfly's Ball*. It was first published in 1807. Picturebook versions of it are still available.

THE BUTTERFLY'S BALL
AND THE GRASSHOPPER'S FEAST

Come take up your hats, and away let us haste,
To the Butterfly's Ball, and the Grasshopper's Feast.
The Trumpeter Gad-fly has summon'd the crew,
And the revels are now only waiting for you.
On the smooth-shaven grass by the side of a wood,
Beneath a broad oak which for ages has stood,
See the children of earth, and the tenants of air,
To the evening's amusement together repair.
And there came the beetle so blind and so black,
Who carried the emmet, his friend on his back.
And there came the gnat, and the dragon-fly too,
And all their relations, green, orange and blue.
And there came the moth, with her plumage of down,
And the hornet, with jacket of yellow and brown,
Who with him the wasp, his companion did bring.
But they promis'd that ev'ning, to lay by their sting.
Then the sly little dormouse peep'd out of his hole,
And led to the feast, his blind cousin the mole.
And the snail, with her horns peeping out of her shell,
Came fatigued with the distance the length of an ell.
A mushroom the table, and on it was spread,
A water-dock leaf, which their table cloth made.
The viands were various to each of their taste,
And the bee brought the honey to sweeten the feast.
With steps most majestic the snail did advance,
And he promised the gazers a minuet to dance:
But they all laugh'd so loud that he drew in his head,
And went in his own little chamber to bed.
Then as evening gave way, to the shadows of night,
Their watchman, the glo-worm came out with his light.
So home let us hasten, while yet we can see:
For no watchman is waiting for you or for me.

TOYS AND GAMES

Butterfly nets were likely to be made at home, as were many other play things. Manufactured toys began to appear in the colony when it was about forty years old. The early arrivals from Britain had few toys, but plenty of games came with them tucked into memories. And so they played ...

Hide and seek, chasings, skittles, leap frog and cricket. Hop-skip-and-jump, see-saw, marbles, mud pies and swinging. Skipping, spinning tops, fighting and wrestling, bowling hoops, swimming and rowing, fishing, football and asking riddles.

Riddles

The more you take, the more you leave
behind.
What is that?   *Footprints.*

What comes in a minute, twice in a moment
but never in a hundred years?   *The letter M.*

What is higher than a house and looks
smaller than a mouse?   *A star in the sky.*

Buck Buck

Another guessing game was called *Buck Buck*. It's as old as the hills. Some people think it goes back to Roman Britain. This is how to play.

Clench both fists and hide them behind your back. Poke out one or more fingers and say to the other player,
    "Buck, Buck!
    How many fingers have I up?"
If the answer is correct then it's that person's turn. Bad luck if the answer isn't right. Start all over again.

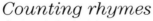

Bad Luck

Colonial children said it was bad luck to say the Lord's Prayer backwards because it could bring the devil to life. And it was bad luck to walk under a ladder. That sounds familiar doesn't it?

Colonial children said however, it was good luck to find a horseshoe, good luck to find a lucky stone. That was spat on, then thrown over the left shoulder. Bad luck if it hit anyone!

Crossed fingers, touching wood, carrying a tiny lump of coal or finding a four leaf clover all warded off bad luck.

Counting rhymes

Colonial children counted the buttons on a new coat, or a dress, or beads on a necklace. And they chanted,

"Solja, sailor, tinker, tailor, gentleman, apothecary, plough boy, thief!"

The last button predicted the future career of the buttons' owner, or told little girls who they were destined to marry. You may have chanted something similar when counting cherry stones. Sure as sure, your grown-ups will have done so. A good many children's games never need books to pass them on. And just as you now use counting rhymes to decide who is to be *In* or *It* to start off a game, so did the colonial children.

Who comes here?
A grenadier.
What do you want?
A pot of beer.
Where's your money?
I forgot.
Get you gone,
You drunken sot.
O . . U . . T!

Doctor, doctor,
How's your wife?
Very bad upon my life.
Can she eat a piece of pie?
Yes, she can and so can I.
O . . U . . T!

Old Soldier from Botany Bay

This game needs someone to be *It*. That person prowls round the outside of a circle of players while they shout, "Here comes an old soldier from Botany Bay. What do you have to give him today?"

The answer is the name and colour of a garment someone is wearing, such as a red dress. Up the person gets and runs round the circle, chased by the old soldier trying to catch the runner before he or she can return. The colours of black, white or grey must not be used. O.U.T. otherwise!

Tin Soldiers

Tin soldiers were favourite toys for a long time, so children enjoyed Hans Christian Andersen's *The Brave Tin Soldier*. His story was first published in Danish in 1838. It wasn't until 1846 that English children could read it. Have you met him yet?

Wooden soldiers

A wooden soldier can be made from a dolly clothes peg.

Paint him, or use felt pens.

Experiment with a clip peg, too. It can become a clip for papers later.

Paper soldiers

Fold a narrow strip of paper into eight parts.

Draw half of a soldier on the fold.

Cut him out but don't cut through his hands and feet

Open out the paper and you should have a row of soldiers.

A ballerina can be made in the same way.

Children enjoyed paper cutting at one time, often using coloured papers, then gluing their work into albums they called *scrap albums*, a collection of paper pictures.

Instant toys

As well as homemade soldiers, colonial
children had wooden carts made by some
kindly adult. Vines became skipping ropes if
the real thing couldn't be found. A plank over
a fallen tree trunk made a see-saw, small
pieces of wood with a skewer mast and rag
sail magically became a boat, or ropes tied to
a branch became a swing. A ring off a barrel
turned into a hoop and Mamma's broom was
borrowed as a horse. Sometimes, an old
stocking or sock was pulled over the head of
a broom to make a quick horse. String was
used for reins and the rider was off and away.
Belts tied to chairs, or to bed posts became
horses for many youngsters to gallop.

ROCKING-HORSE

When Charles had done reading
His books every day,
Then he goes with his hoop
In the garden to play;
Or, his whip in his hand
Quickly mounts up across
And gallops away
On his fine rocking-horse.

WOODEN DOLLS AND ALL

Jane Davis who sailed on the *Scarborough* with the First Fleet may have owned a Flander's Baby, a wooden Dutch doll that had been made in the Netherlands.

"The children of England took pleasure in breaking
What the children of Holland took pleasure in making."

Later, Queen Victoria as a child, owned 132 of these simple little dolls and dressed 32 of them herself. She liked them better than the expensive dolls with moulded heads of china, glass eyes and human hair. Hands and feet were also moulded but the rest of the doll was kid or cloth, stuffed with sawdust.

Elizabeth Macarthur well may have owned such a doll, but most of the colony's children made do with rag dolls, a dressed-up spoon or stick, or a quickly made handkerchief doll.

Here's how it was made.

You'll need a big handkerchief, cotton-wool balls and five small elastic bands.

Spread out the handkerchief on a flat surface.

Put the cotton-wool ball in the centre.

Fasten it in place with an elastic band. That makes the doll's head.

Take up a corner and bunch it off with an elastic band. That makes one arm.

Make the second arm from the opposite corner, or use knots instead of bands.

Make the legs in the same way and there's the hanky doll.

1.   2.   3.   4.

86

THE ADVENTURES OF A LONDON DOLL

A wooden doll with movable arms and legs was made by a skilled craftsman called Sprat. Mrs Sprat painted her eyes and eyebrows, the eldest son glued on her hair, the second son fitted her jointed arms and legs into place with pegs and their little sister painted her rosy cheeks and lips. Then her complexion was thoroughly hardened with enamel until she was a doll fit in all respects for the most polished society.

Maria Poppet was sold to a toy shop and left on a shelf for what seemed like years then ... but she can tell the story herself.

"One afternoon Emmy had been reading to her sister as usual. This time the story had been about a great emperor in France who had a great many soldiers to play with, and whose name was Napoleon Bonaparte. The master of the shop listened to this, and as he walked thoughtfully up and down from the back room to the shop in front he made himself a cocked hat of brown paper, and put it on his head, with the corners pointing to each shoulder. Emmy continued to read, and the master continued thoughtfully walking up and down with his hands behind him, one hand holding the other.

Presently, and when his walk had led him into the front shop, where I could not see him, the shop-bell rang and Emmy ceased reading. A boy came in, and the following dialogue took place.

'If you please, sir,' said the voice of a boy, 'do you want a twelfth-cake?'

'Not particularly,' answered the master, 'but I have no objection to one.'

'What will you give for it, sir?' said the boy.

'That is quite another question,' answered the master. 'But go about your business. I am extremely engaged.'

'I do not want money for it, sir,' said the boy.

'What do you mean by that, my little captain?' said the master.

'Why, sir,' said the boy, 'if you please, I want a nice doll for my little sister. I will give you this large twelfth-cake that I have in paper here for a good doll.'

'Let me see the cake,' said the master. 'So, how did you get this cake?'

'My grandfather is a pastry-cook, sir,' answered the boy. 'My sister and I live with him. I went today to take home seven twelfth-cakes. But the family at one house had all gone away out of the country, and locked up the house, and forgotten to send for the cake. So grandfather told me that I and my sister might have it.'

'What's your name?'

'Thomas Plummy, sir. I live in Bishopgatestreet, near the Flower Pot.'

'Very well, Thomas Plummy. You may choose any doll you fancy from that case.'

Here some time elapsed. While the boy was choosing, the master continued his slow walk to and fro from one room to the other, with the brown paper cocked hat still on his head. It was so very light that he did not feel it, and had forgotten it was there. At last the boy declared he did not like any of the dolls in the case. So he went from one case to another, refusing all those the master offered him. When he did choose one himself the master said it was too expensive. Presently the master said he had another box full of good dolls in the back room. In he came, looking so grave in his cocked hat, and began to open a long wooden box. But the boy followed him to the door, and peeping in suddenly, called out, 'There, sir! That one! That is the doll for my cake!' He pointed his little brown finger up at me.

'Aha!' said the master, 'that one is also too expensive; I cannot let you have that.'

However, he took me down, and while the boy was looking at me with evident satisfaction, as if his mind was quite made up, the master got a knife and pushed the point of it into the side of the cake, just to see if it was as good inside as it seemed to be on the outside. During all this time he never once recollected that he had on the brown cocked hat.

'Now,' said the master, taking me out of the boy's hand, and holding me at arm's length, 'you must give me the cake and two shillings beside for this doll. This is a young lady of superior make, is this doll. Made by one of the first makers. The celebrated Sprat, the only maker, I may say, of these kinds of jointed dolls. See! All the joints move. All work the proper way — up and down, backwards and forwards, any way you please. See what lovely blue eyes, what rosy cheeks and lips and what a complexion on the neck, face, hands and arms. The hair is also of the most beautiful kind of delicate light-brown curl that can possibly be found. You never before saw such a doll, nor any of your relations. It is something, I can tell you, to have such a doll in a family. If you were to buy her, she would cost you a matter of twelve shillings!'

The boy, without a moment's hesitation, took the cake and held it out flat on the palm of his hand, balancing it as if to show how heavy it was. 'Sir,' he said, 'this is a twelfth-cake of very superior make. If the young lady who sits reading there was only to taste it, she would say so too. It was made by my grandfather himself, who is known to be one of the first makers in all Bishopgatestreet. I may say the very first. There is no better in all the world. You see how heavy it is. What a quantity of plums, currants, butter, sugar and orange and lemon-peel there is in it, besides brandy and carraway comfits. See! What beautiful frost-work of white sugar there is all over the top and sides! See, too what characters there are, and made in sugar of all colours! Kings and queens sit on their thrones, and lions and dogs, and Jem Crow, and Swiss cottages in winter, and railway carriages and girls with tambourines, and a village steeple with a cow looking in at the porch. All these standing or walking, or dancing upon white sugar, surrounded with curling twists and true lovers knots in pink and green citron, with damson cheese and black currant paste

between. You never saw such a cake before, sir, and I'm sure none of your family ever smelt any cake like it. It's quite a nosegay for the Queen Victoria herself. If you were to buy it at grandfather's shop you would have to pay fifteen shillings and more for it.'

'Thomas Plummy!' said the master, looking very earnestly at the boy. 'Thomas Plummy! Take the doll, and give me the cake. I only hope it may prove half as good as you say. And it is my opinion that, if you, Thomas Plummy, should not happen to be sent to New South Wales to bake brown bread, you may some day or other come to be Lord Mayor of London.'

'Thank you, sir,' said the boy. 'How many *Abernethy biscuits will you take for your cocked hat?'

The master instantly put his hand up to his head, looking so confused and vexed, and the boy ran laughing out of the shop. At the door he was met by his sister, who had been waiting to receive me in her arms. Ellen Plummy called me Maria Poppet and I was to have many adventures."

Abernethy biscuits were small, round and flat, made with arrowroot and carraway seeds.
Twelfth-cake must have been some cake! It was eaten on Twelfth night, 6th January, the last day of Christmas when it was celebrated for 12 days.

CHRISTMAS

No snow, no holly, no ivy belonged to a colonial Christmas. Instead, bunches of gum leaves festooned veranda posts and doorways, and bowls filled with Christmas bush and Christmas bells decorated rooms where the ceilings were hung with lengths of coloured paper chains, usually made by the children who used flour-and-water paste. A narrow strip of paper was pasted into a loop shape. The next strip of paper slipped through that loop, then it too was glued. You could try that. Very small chains look pretty on a Christmas tree.

Christmas gifts were usually modest, often food for adults and small things for children. Oranges, sweets and a coin often were stuffed into a stocking or sock.

From the earliest Christmas in Australia people nostalgically ate an English dinner of turkey and plum pudding, but sensible folk took their feast out-doors. The rich pudding, thick with fruit and silver tokens or coins, had boiled for hours, inside a cloth, in the family copper.

PUDDIN'S SONG

O, who would be a puddin',
A puddin' in a pot,
A puddin' which is stood on
A fire which is hot?
O sad indeed the lot
Of puddin's in a pot.

It would be cooler out of doors, but it also meant an unending battle with flies — blowflies, bush flies, sand flies *and* mosquitoes.

A HUNGRY SWARM

Being plagued by mosquitoes one day,
Said old Fox, "Pray, don't send them away,
For a hungrier swarm
Would work in more harm.
I'd rather the full ones would stay."

Children, particularly babies, slept under protective voluminous mosquito nets and little boys often wore flannel night shirts. *Phew!*

However, something else was blamed for disturbing the sleep of the good people of Melbourne who lived near the Botanic Gardens.

BUNYIP

"Some unknown animal, most probably the bunyip, has located himself in the lake at the foot of the Botanic Gardens and for several nights past has disturbed residents in that vicinity. Here is a rare chance for some of our sporting nimrods; there can be no great difficulty in beating up the monster's quarters when we have got him so snugly ensconced so close to the city, and nothing short of immortal fame will be the reward of the man who first furnishes a veritable Bunyip for the Museum of the Mechanics' Institution."

We don't know if the bunyip took off in fright, but many a lonely shepherd felt tingles down his spine when an eerie unexplained howl awakened him.

THE BUNYIP

Far off in lonely Tuckianne Swamp the
   awful bunyip cries;
His home is in the tall green reeds
   where deep water lies.
There, safe among the shady trees,
   beneath the verdant mud,
He sleeps all day and wakes at night
   to gambol in the flood.
His body's like a yearling colt; his claws
   are sharp and strong;
His tail is like a rough pine log some
   nine or ten feet long;
His head is long, his neck is thick,
   with long waving mane,
And those who ever saw him once ne'er
   wish to look again.

BUSHRANGERS

Towards the middle of the 1800's no more convicts were sent to Australia. It was the end of free labour. Life was back-breakingly hard for many settlers. Then, gold was discovered.

People poured into the gold-fields from all over the world, all hoping to dig up a fortune. A few did. Most didn't. It was back to living in tents, eating poor food, water shortages and bushrangers who found it easier to rob than to dig for gold.

"I'm sure I'll not be found

Hunting nuggets in the ground," boasted Jack le Froy.

The bushrangers often had flamboyant names, such as Starlight, Thunderbolt, Captain Moonlight and Sam Poo. All of them were scoundrels, including Ned Kelly, Dan Morgan and the Wild Colonial Boy.

FIFTY BURLY BUSHRANGERS

Fifty burly bushrangers
  Went out to steal some gold,
But all the bush was wet with dew
  And one caught a cold.
And one found a bulldog ant
  Creeping in his chest,
And one had a *gammsky* leg
  And had to have a rest.
One thought he saw a snake,
  Another had a pain,
The rest, they heard a gun go off
  And scampered home again.

Isobel Kendall Bowden

BOILED MUTTON AND DAMPER

And what did the miners eat? Boiled mutton and damper, as often as not. The damper was made in the ashes of a campfire. Here's a recipe.

3 cups of self-raising flour.
I teaspoon of salt.
1¼ cups of milk, or water.

Mix the flour and salt into a dough with the milk. Press the damper into a round cake shape and bake it in the ashes for half an hour. Add some raisins at Christmas.

If you decide to make a damper, put it on a greased scone tray and bake at 190°C (375°F) for about 30 minutes. The damper is cooked when it sounds hollow when tapped.

Eat it with butter, or Cocky's joy (golden syrup), or Kidman's blood (tomato sauce). Yummy!

Miners and squatters, drovers and shearers, swagmen, bullockies, rouseabouts, just about everyone ate damper, often with slabs of corned beef and washed down with sweet black tea.

Bread was for town folk where the familiar British food was still eaten. Roast meats and stews cooked on fuel stoves, were likely to be served during a heat wave. Second course would be apple tart, or a stodgy pudding with custard. Meat was eaten three times daily, in the bush.

STEAK AND EGGS

Steak and eggs for breakfast,
Steak and eggs for tea,
With a loaf of bread
As big as your head
And a lousy cup of tea.

The dog got the scraps.

A TERRIBLE SINNER

My old dog is a terrible sinner
He sneaks under the table
And tries to steal dinner.

Every country family owned dogs. A working dog was often as
useful as a man, and valued. Invariably, a sheep dog was
called Lassie or Laddie, Bonnie or Mac. Cattle dogs were Blue,
Prince or Jack, or Bess.

FLEA-BAG

I've got a dog as thin as a rail.
He's got fleas all over his tail.
Every time the tail goes flop
The fleas on the bottom hop to the top.

GOOD DOG, BESS!

Bob, the drover, had a dog called Bess. It was about the time when there were more sheep in the country than people and Bob was moving a huge mob of sheep to market. He'd been on the road for weeks, all by himself, and about three hundred of the ewes were about to lamb. What's more Bess was about to have pups, so he left her in charge of the lambing ewes at a waterhole where there was plenty of good feed. He pushed on with the rest of the mob.

Three weeks later he was riding back, down the track, having sold the sheep, and he was wondering about Bess. Would you believe it, along trotted Bess with three hundred ewes, and there wasn't a lamb in sight, but he knew what kind of a dog Bess was, and sent her on to town with her mob. He kept going back down the track and that afternoon he saw a little cloud of dust.

Out of the dust ran a mob of lambs and they were being driven by five pups. Bess' pups! Well, I told you that he knew she was a good dog!

A SHEARER BLOKE

A shearer bloke from Yarrapeet
Was noted for his great big feet.
When grubs or locusts plagued the land
The shearer bloke was in demand
       to stamp,
          stamp,
             stamp.

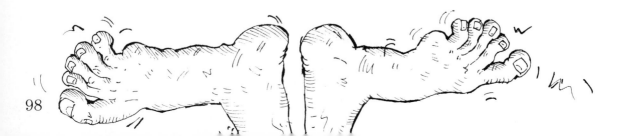

CLICK GO THE SHEARS

Traditional

Out on the board the old shear-er stands,

Grasp - ing his shears in his thin, bo - ny hands;

Fixed is his gaze on a bare - bel - lied yeo,

Glo - ry if he gets her, won't he make the 'ring-er' go!

Click go the shears boys, click, click, click;

Wide is his blow and his hands move quick, The

ring-er looks a - round and is beat -en by a blow, And

cur - ses the old snag-ger with the bare bel - lied yeo.

FIVE MILES FROM GUNDAGAI

Bullockies with their towering drays of baled wool, swayed over track-roads from properties to wool stores. The dray was an important form of transport, and every child knew that their drivers, encouraging the straining bullocks pulling loads, were notorious swearers who could just about turn the air blue!

Bill was such a man, but it's his dog who is famous, yet his name hasn't gone down in history. One of Bill's bullocks was called Nobby and the nameless dog was supposed to have disgraced himself out of Gundagai, but bushmen defend that dog. No working dog would use a tucker box as a loo!

Across the hills and plains,
    I've teamed outback this forty years
In blazin' droughts and rains,
    I've lived a heap of trouble down
Without a bloomin' lie,
    But I can't forget what happened me
Five miles from Gundagai.
    T'was gettin' dark,
    The team got bogged,
    The axle snapped in two;
    Lost me matches and me pipe,
    So what was I to do?
The rain came on, t'was bitter cold
    And hungry too was I,
And the dog sat on the Tucker Box
    Five miles from Gundagai.

Today the dog sits on the tucker box, outside Gundagai as a memorial to all the working dogs Australia has known.

PETS

Townsfolk kept dogs, too. It was said that every family in Bathurst had at least five dogs, plus cats to hunt for rats and mice. Children kept pet chooks, ponies, lambs and calves. Occasionally someone gave a child a pet lizard, emu, galah or cockatoo, but a kangaroo like this one of young Meg's is most unlikely. *It lapped milk from his bowl and pecked a bone like a monkey.* Meg and kangaroo belonged to an 1832 story book called *The happy grandmother and her grandchildren who went to Australia,* written by Peter Prattle in England. He never visited Australia!

W. A. C. came to South Australia a few years later and he became the author of one of our earliest picture books. He based it on an old rhyme.

WHO KILLED COCKATOO?

Who killed Cockatoo?
I, said the Mawpawk,
With my tomahawk.
I killed Cockatoo.

Who saw him die?
I, said the Opossum,
From the gum-blossom.
I saw him die.

Who caught his blood?
I, said the Lark,
With this piece of bark.
I caught his blood.

Who'll make his shroud?
I, said the Eagle,
With my thread and needle.
I'll make his shroud.

Who'll be chief mourner?
I, said the Plover,
For I was his lover.
I'll be chief mourner.

Who'll dig his grave?
I, said the Wombat,
My nails for my spade.
I'll dig his grave.

Who'll say a prayer?
I, said the magpie,
My best I will try.
I'll say a prayer.

Who'll bear him to his tomb?
I, said the Platypus,
On my back, gently, thus.
I'll bear him to his tomb.

Who'll be the parson?
I, said the Crow,
Solemn and slow.
I'll be the parson.

Who'll carry the link?
I, said the Macaw,
With my little paw.
I'll carry the link.

Who'll chant a psalm?
I, said the Black Swan,
I'll sing his death song.
I'll chant a psalm.

Who'll watch in the night?
I, said the Wild Dog,
As he crept from a log.
I'll watch in the night.

Who'll toll the bell?
I, said the Pelican,
Again and again.
I'll toll the bell.

Then droop'd every head,
And ceas'd every song,
As onward they sped,
All mournful along.

All join in a ring,
With wing linking wing,
And trilling and twittering,
Around the grave sing:

  Alas! Cockatoo,
How low dost thou lie;
  A long, sad adieu.
A fond parting sigh!

COCKATOO SOUP

First find a dead cockatoo. Put it in a pot over a camp fire but first cover the bird with creek water. Add some nice flat river stones. Boil for five hours. Six, seven, eight or nine hours improves the flavour. Throw out the cocky. Throw out the water. Eat the stones with pepper and salt.

SCHOOL SKIRT

A cocky's daughter from Sale
Made a skirt of hay from a bale,
But a marauding young calf
Ate her school skirt in half,
And the rest blew away in a gale.

Cocky was a name given to dairy farmers, as well as parrots.

SCHOOL

Children didn't wear uniforms to school. And their clothing was still similiar to adults'. When Mumma wore a hooped skirt so did her daughter. When Mumma's skirt had a bustle that shaped her like a duck, her little girls wore skirts that were very full at the back. A chemise went underneath, so did drawers and long stockings. No one dared to show a bare leg! Later on dresses were kept clean by huge, snowy-white, frilled aprons that were stiff with starch. There were shawls for cold days and parasols and broad-brimmed hats for hot weather.

From the middle of the 1800's school was compulsory but some children only attended when it suited the family. Children stayed at home to do farm work but could officially leave school when 12 years old.

THE OLD BARK SCHOOL

It was built of bark and poles, and the floor was full of holes
Where each leak in rainy weather made a pool;
And the walls were mainly cracks lined with calico and sacks,
There was little need for windows in the school.

Then we rode to school and back by the rugged gully-track,
On the old grey horse that carried three or four;
And he looked so very wise that he lit the master's eyes
Every time he put his head in at the door.

And we learnt the world in scraps from some ancient dingy
      maps,
Long discarded by the public schools in town;
And as nearly every book dated back to Captain Cook
Our geography was somewhat upside down.

Aboriginal children were taken from their families who often now lived on land reserved for them. It was hoped to educate the children to the European way of living.

All children still wrote on slates. A smelly sponge or rag might be used to clean them. Spit and a wipe over with a sweeping elbow or fist was quicker! Graduation was to pen and ink, using thick or lean strokes according to a copy-book.

Parents paid large fees for the children who attended private and boarding schools where little girls also learned the social graces and deportment, pianoforte, singing and reciting. These accomplishments were aired when the family entertained. Little boys considered they were better off, even if they had to learn Latin and Greek.

And the luckiest children owned a copy of *Alice in Wonderland.* Here's Alice about to meet the Mock Turtle.

THE MOCK TURTLE'S STORY

So they went up to the Mock Turtle, who looked at them with large eyes full of tears, but said nothing.

"This here young lady," said the Gryphon, "she wants for to know your history, she do."

"I'll tell it her," said the Mock Turtle, in a deep hollow tone; "sit down, both of you, and don't speak a word till I've finished."

So they sat down, and nobody spoke for some minutes. Alice thought to herself, "I don't see how he can *ever* finish, if he doesn't begin." But she waited patiently.

"Once," said the Mock Turtle at last, with a deep sigh, "I was a real Turtle."

These words were followed by a very long silence, broken only by an occasional exclamation of "Hjckrrh!" from the Gryphon, and the constant sobbing of the Mock Turtle. Alice was very nearly getting up and saying, "Thank you, sir, for your interesting story," but she could not help thinking there *must* be more to come, so she sat still and said nothing.

"When we were little," the Mock Turtle went on at last, more calmly though still sobbing a little now and then, "we went to school in the sea. The master was an old Turtle — we used to call him Tortoise..."

"Why did you call him Tortoise, if he wasn't one?" Alice asked.

"We called him Tortoise because he taught us," said the Mock Turtle angrily. "Really you are very dull!"

"You ought to be ashamed of yourself for asking such a simple question," added the Gryphon; and then they both sat silent and looked at poor Alice, who felt ready to sink into the earth. At last the Gryphon said to the Mock Turtle, "Drive on, old fellow. Don't be all day about it!" and he went on with these words.

"Yes, we went to school in the sea, though you mayn't believe it..."

"I never said I didn't," interrupted Alice.

"You did," said the Mock Turtle.

"Hold your tongue!" added the Gryphon, before Alice could speak again. The Mock Turtle went on:

"We had the best of educations — in fact, we went to school every day..."

"*I've* been to day-school, too," said Alice; "you needn't be so proud as all that."

"With extras?" asked the Mock Turtle, a little anxiously.

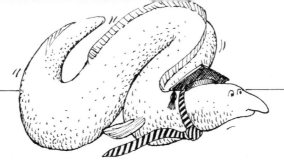

"Yes," said Alice, "we learned French and Music."

"And washing?" said the Mock Turtle.

"Certainly not!" cried Alice indignantly.

"Ah! then yours wasn't a really good school," said the Mock Turtle in a tone of great relief, "Now at *ours* they had at the end of the bill — French, music, *and washing* — extra."

"You couldn't have wanted it much," said Alice; "living at the bottom of the sea."

"I couldn't afford to learn it," said the Mock Turtle, with a sigh. "I only took the regular course."

"What was that?" inquired Alice.

"Reeling and Writhing, of course, to begin with," the Mock Turtle replied; "and then the different branches of Arithmetic — Ambition, Distraction, Uglification and Derision."

"Never heard of Uglification," Alice ventured to say. "What is it?"

The Gryphon lifted up both its paws in surprise. "Never heard of uglifying!" it exclaimed. "You know what to beautify is, I suppose?"

"Yes," said Alice doubtfully, "it means — to — make — anything — prettier."

"Well, then," the Gryphon went on, "if you don't know what to uglify is, you must be a simpleton."

Alice did not feel encouraged to ask any more questions about it, so she turned to the Mock Turtle and said, "What else did you learn?"

"Well, there was Mystery," the Mock Turtle replied, counting off the subjects on his flappers — "Mystery, ancient and modern, with Seaography, then Drawling — the Drawling-master was an old conger-eel, that used to come once a week. *He* taught us Drawling, Stretching, and Fainting in Coils."

"What was *that* like?" said Alice.

"Well, I can't show it to you myself," the Mock Turtle said, "I'm too stiff. And the Gryphon never learnt it."

"Hadn't time," said the Gryphon; "I went to the Classical Master, though. He was an old crab, *he* was."

"I never went to him," the Mock Turtle said, with a sigh, "he taught Laughing and Grief, they used to say."

"So he did, so he did," said the Gryphon, sighing in his turn; and both creatures hid their faces in their paws.

"And how many hours a day did you do lessons?" said Alice, in a hurry to change the subject.

"Ten hours the first day," said the Mock Turtle; "nine hours the next, and so on."

"What a curious plan!" exclaimed Alice.

"That's the reason they're called lessons," the Gryphon remarked; "because they lessen from day to day."

This was quite a new idea to Alice, and she thought it over a little before she made her next remark. "Then the eleventh day must have been a holiday?"

"Of course it was," said the Mock Turtle.

"And how did you manage on the twelfth?" Alice went on eagerly.

"That's enough about lessons," the Gryphon interrupted in a very decided tone; "tell her something about the games now."

FAVOURITE GAMES AND TOYS

Jacks

Knuckle bones cost nothing. Children collected them from the family's dinner of roast leg of lamb. The bones were dyed or painted in a variety of colours. Here's how to play. Use one hand only!

A set of five bones was called *Jacks*.

Hold the Jacks in one hand.

Throw the Jacks upwards, flipping up the palm with fingers slightly spread.

Catch the Jacks. Have three or more tries.

It is a competition to see who can catch the largest number of Jacks.

There are many *Jacks* games. Ask around. Some of your adults would have been experts with *Jacks*.

Bumpo

Bumpo is more boisterous.

A circle is drawn.

Children follow it, hopping on one leg with arms folded and trying to knock an opponent out of the ring.

The one who lasts longest and doesn't topple over, is the winner.

For quieter times indoors there were games, such as ludo and backgammon, hunt the feather, draughts and chess, paper cutting, paper dolls and indoor cricket, wooden blocks and blowing soap bubbles, printing sets and lantern slides, charades, toy theatres, Punch and Judy and jigsaw puzzles. Some little girls had beautiful dolls' houses and perhaps a doll with a wax head that melted if it was left near a fire. And there were *sleepers*, dolls that opened and shut their eyes.

Apple dolls

Homemade dolls were fashioned from clothes pegs, dusters, scarves and handkerchiefs, old turnips or windfall apples. Two apples were skewered together and given a dandelion hat and a daisy chain necklace. Eyes and mouth were bits of twig. Arms and legs would be twigs, as well.

MATCH BOX TOYS

When children could get hold of match boxes they made toys for themselves or a dolls' house. It could be an upturned box, or a grand upstairs-downstairs model. It was the big time for dolls' mansions. Queen Mary's is on view at Windsor Castle.

Chest of drawers
Six complete match boxes were glued together in two sets of three.
   The tops and sides were covered with a long strip of fancy paper.
   The trays were the drawers and split pins became knobs.

Train
At least three complete match boxes were needed so they could be strung together as shown. Corks were glued on one box for an engine. Sometimes wheels of cardboard were pinned on the engine and carriages but the train worked well without wheels, puffing along an imaginary line.

Clock
Just the box was used. It could be covered with paper or painted. Cardboard hands were fixed with a split pin loose enough to point to the hours that were drawn into position.

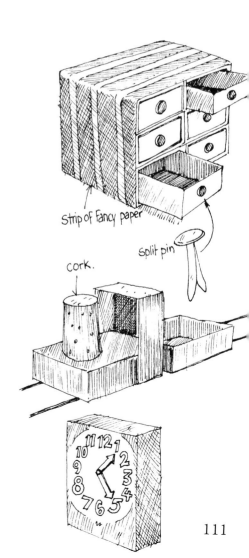

strip of fancy paper

split pin

cork.

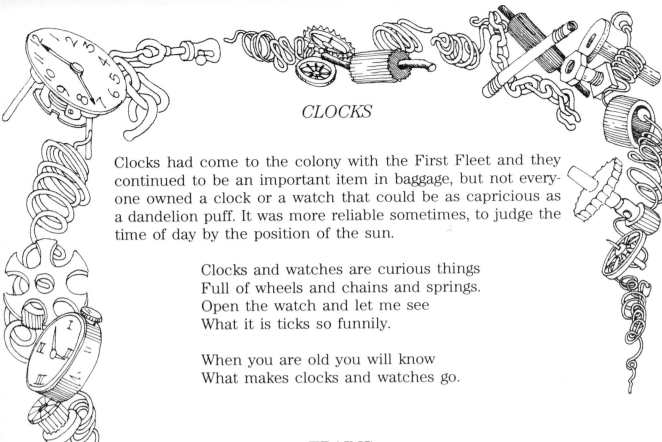

CLOCKS

Clocks had come to the colony with the First Fleet and they continued to be an important item in baggage, but not everyone owned a clock or a watch that could be as capricious as a dandelion puff. It was more reliable sometimes, to judge the time of day by the position of the sun.

> Clocks and watches are curious things
> Full of wheels and chains and springs.
> Open the watch and let me see
> What it is ticks so funnily.
>
> When you are old you will know
> What makes clocks and watches go.

TRAINS

Trains seemed to have trouble with timetables. There was great excitement when the first trains puffed along their tracks. As the lines fanned out across the country the individual colonies had to synchronise clocks for efficient running of the trains.

THE COW WAS ON THE RAILWAY TRACK

> The cow was on the railway track,
> A train was coming fast.
> The train got off the railway track
> To let the cow go past.

SMOKE RINGS AND TUNNELS

All children knew that to see a smoke ring from an engine it was time to make a quick wish — it would come true!

A shunting train meant good luck. If there were two engines working, then it was *double good luck*.

It was bad luck to walk over a bridge when a train ran underneath. Fingers were crossed to break the bad luck, and kept crossed until that child saw a dog.

Never speak when a train rushes through a tunnel. Children vowed it brought bad luck. It certainly did if a window was open. In came cinders and choking smoke!

DOT AND THE KANGAROO

None of this knowledge was of use to a little girl called Dot. Her transport was by kangaroo and here's part of her story.

But first, you need to know that Dot was lost. She found a friend, a kangaroo, and was carried in her pouch, in place of a lost joey. This adventure begins when they hear Aborigines holding a corroboree. They creep close and...

After more dancing to the singing and noise of the onlookers, a Black Fellow came from the little bower in the dim background, with a battered straw hat on, and a few rags tied round his neck and wrists, in imitation of a collar and cuffs. The fellow tried to act the part of a white man, although he had no more clothes on but that old hat and rags. But, after a great deal of dancing, he strutted about, pulled up the rag collar, made a great fuss with his rag cuffs, and kept taking off his old straw hat to the other Black Fellows, and to the rest of the tribe, who kept up the noise on the other side of the fires.

"Now this is better!" said the Kangaroo, with a smile. "It's very silly, but Willy Wagtail says that is just the way Humans go on in the town. Black Humans can act being white Humans, but they are no good as kangaroos."

Dot thought that if men behaved like that in town it must be very strange. She had not seen any like the acting Black Fellow at her cottage home. But she did not say anything, for it was quite clear in her little mind that Black Fellows, kangaroos, and willy wagtails had a very poor opinion of white people. She felt that they must all be wrong; but, all the same, she sometimes wished she could be a noble kangaroo, and not a despised human being.

"I wish I were not a little white girl," she whispered to the Kangaroo.

The gentle animal patted her kindly with her delicate black hands. "You are as nice now as my baby kangaroo," she said sadly, "but you will have to grow into a real white Human. For some reason there have to be all sorts of creatures on earth. There are hawks, snakes, dingoes, and humans, and no one can tell for what good they exist. They must have dropped on to this world by mistake for another, where there could only have been themselves. After all," said the kind animal, "it wouldn't do for every one to be a kangaroo, for I doubt if there would be enough grass; but you may become an improved Human."

"How could I be that?" asked Dot eagerly.

"Never wear kangaroo leather boots — never use kangaroo skin rugs, and" — here it hesitated a little, as though the subject were a most unpleasant one to mention.

"Never do what?" inquired Dot, anxious to know all that she should do, so as to be improved.

"Never, never eat kangaroo-tail soup!" said the Kangaroo, solemnly.

"I never will,' said Dot, earnestly, 'I will be an improved Human."

This conversation had been so serious to both Dot and the Kangaroo that they had quite forgotten the perilousness of their position. Perhaps this was because the Kangaroo cannot think, but it quickly jumped to the conclusion that they were in danger.

Whilst they had been peeping at the corroboree, and talking, the dingo dogs that had been prowling around the camp had caught the scent of the Kangaroo; and, following the trail, had set up an angry snapping and howling.

The instant this sound was heard by the Kangaroo, she made an immense bound, and as she seemed to fly through the bush, Dot could hear the sounds of the corroboree give place to a noise of shouting and disorder: the dingo dogs and the Blacks were all in pursuit, and Dot's Kangaroo, with little Dot in her pouch, was leaping and bounding at a terrific pace to save both their lives!

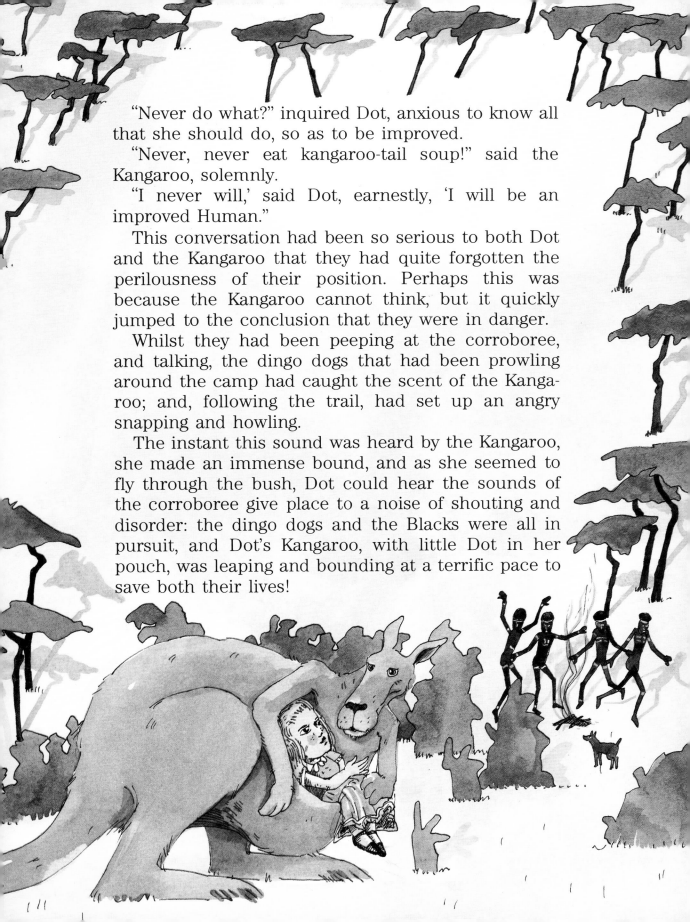

OLD JUMPETY-BUMPETY HOP-AND-GO-ONE

Old Jumpety-Bumpety Hop-and-Go-One
Was lying asleep on his side in the sun.
This old kangaroo, he was whisking the flies
With his long glossy tail, from his ears and his eyes.
Jumpety-Bumpety Hop-and-Go-One
Was lying asleep on his side in the sun.

MY UNCLE ROASTED A KANGAROO

My uncle roasted a kangaroo.
Gave me the gristly end to chew.
Was that a very nice thing to do,
To give me the gristly end of kangaroo — to chew?

Roared out at camp fires to a melody from Gounod's *Faust.*

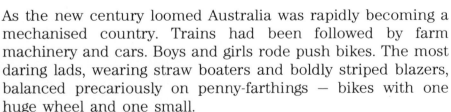

As the new century loomed Australia was rapidly becoming a mechanised country. Trains had been followed by farm machinery and cars. Boys and girls rode push bikes. The most daring lads, wearing straw boaters and boldly striped blazers, balanced precariously on penny-farthings — bikes with one huge wheel and one small.

Girls bowled along more sedately, still hampered by long skirts but modestly wearing bloomers underneath. These were very roomy pants, gathered into the knee with elastic. It still was shocking to show too much leg. Daisy rode on a tandem, a two seater bike. Lots of grown-ups know her song. Ask around.

DAISY

Daisy, Daisy, give me your answer do,
I'm half crazy all for the love of you.
It won't be a stylish marriage,
I can't afford a carriage,
But you'll look sweet,
Upon the seat
Of a bicycle built for two.

Cars weren't too popular at first. They frightened the horses.
At one time a man walked in front of a car waving a flag to let
folk know that the horrible thing was approaching. Guess
which tune goes with this car rhyme.

TWINKLE, TWINKLE

Twinkle, twinkle little star,
Daddy drives a rotten car.
Press the starter, pull the choke,
Off we go in a cloud of smoke.
Twinkle, twinkle, little star
Daddy drives a rotten car.

LIZZIE, MY CAR

I love you though your steering gear is faulty,
　I love you though your body creaks and groans;
I love you though your hooter's ceased from hooting,
　I love you though your differential moans;
I love you though your big-ends all are knocking,
　I love you though your tail-lights fail to shine;
I love you though your cushion's hard as blazes —
　I love you, yes, I love you, Lizzie mine.

Precious Tin Lizzies of veteran age are still being driven lovingly. Lucky you to see one in a rally! Who knows, you may even get a chance to ride in a restored car one day. It'll probably be older than its owner!

　　Here lies the body of Emily White
　　Who signalled left
　　And turned to the right.

THE NEW CENTURY

The new century, your century, was to bring the Federation of the Australian states, with a national parliament in Canberra and a national flag. And children chanted:

Australian born, Australian bred.
Long in the leg, thick in the head.
Very funny, terribly rude
Fond of money, extremely shrewd.

It brought faster steam ship travel to Europe and rapid communication with the telegraph. And there was gas lighting followed by electricity, telephones and teddy bears, neck-to-knee bathing costumes, lamingtons and amongst many other surprising things including aeroplanes, came a children's book. It told of the warm relationship between an isolated white woman and Bett-Bett, her *Little Black Princess*. Let's see what happened to Bett-Bett's kittens.

A TALE OF CATS

Bett-Bett had seven kittens ... all her own, she says, for she found them 'by meself'. Well, the very next morning Cheon announced at breakfast time that *he* had found another little family of kittens — five this time — on the foot of his bed when he woke up. 'My word, Missus!' he said, 'I wake up! ... I listen! ... I hear Sing-out, Sing out of my bed! ... I look this way ... that way ...' (And Cheon did it to show us), and

by-and-by I bin catch-em five little-fellow pussy cat on my bed, tucked up with them. Plenty pussy-cat now, I think', Cheon said. 'Too many, I think'; and, gathering them all up — little brother and all — he carried them across to the storehouse verandah, and put them in a big box there, where an old broody hen was already in possession. The broody hen didn't mind at all.

Then, of course, Bett-Bett's little mother pussy found them there, and after a good look carried her own seven kittens across — for company, I suppose. One by one she began to carry them, until Bett-Bett lent a hand with the last four. So there they all were for about a week, two pussy mothers, twelve kittens, and a broody hen, all happy in the one box — and all Bett-Bett's little friends from the camp, too, I think, were gathered round in a ring with her most of the time. And then one night Cheon's little mother cat stole the whole twelve kittens, without the other mother knowing somehow; and Bett-Bett's poor pussy mother was crying, crying everywhere in the morning, and even the old broody hen was clucking everywhere in the fuss.

How ever to find them we couldn't think, for all round us everywhere was just bush, and only bush. But Bett-Bett knew, and steadily began looking, looking everywhere on the ground, and all in and out among our footprints. And then, just saying: 'Come on, my pussy!' (Sue, the dog, of course, was never allowed near the cats), quietly she went away, slowly,

slowly through the grass, with the pussy-cat mother at her heels, seeing, as none of us could see, every bent blade of grass, or little scurry in the dust, where the pussy cat had trodden or a kitten had dragged as she carried it, until with a swift pounce Bett-Bett had found them all, all cosily settled down in an old dead tree-stump, all hidden in a tangle of bush and scrub; and *her* little pussy cat just went in and settled quietly down in the new home as though nothing unusual had happened, and we all went back to the house thinking the story would end there. But the very next morning, when we got up, every pussy cat and kitten, and even the old broody hen, were safely back in their box. Who carried them back we really don't know! Perhaps all helped this time.

Now, was there ever such a Tale of Cats, or such a clever little person as my Bett-Bett!

While children enjoyed Bett-Bett's adventures they were also lapping up *Coles Funny Picture Books*.

PINS IN YOUR TOES

You are so graceful and charming
  So sleek and so fat —
Was there ever yet born
  Such a love of a cat?
You push and you rub
  With your little pink nose;
But I must not forget
You have pins in your toes.

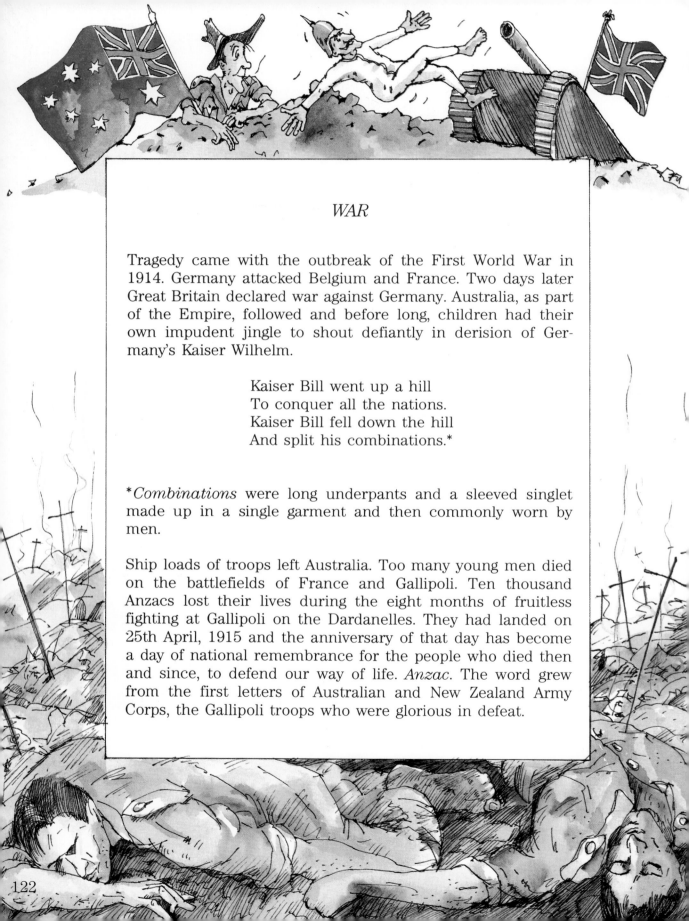

WAR

Tragedy came with the outbreak of the First World War in 1914. Germany attacked Belgium and France. Two days later Great Britain declared war against Germany. Australia, as part of the Empire, followed and before long, children had their own impudent jingle to shout defiantly in derision of Germany's Kaiser Wilhelm.

> Kaiser Bill went up a hill
> To conquer all the nations.
> Kaiser Bill fell down the hill
> And split his combinations.*

Combinations were long underpants and a sleeved singlet made up in a single garment and then commonly worn by men.

Ship loads of troops left Australia. Too many young men died on the battlefields of France and Gallipoli. Ten thousand Anzacs lost their lives during the eight months of fruitless fighting at Gallipoli on the Dardanelles. They had landed on 25th April, 1915 and the anniversary of that day has become a day of national remembrance for the people who died then and since, to defend our way of life. *Anzac*. The word grew from the first letters of Australian and New Zealand Army Corps, the Gallipoli troops who were glorious in defeat.

THE MAN WITH THE DONKEY

Working in pairs, stretcher bearers carried the badly
wounded out of the trenches to the tent hospital on
the beach at Gallipoli. They wore the red cross arm-
band, an international sign of unarmed medical aid.
The noise, the fear, the carnage of death were relent-
less, and somewhere in this horror Jack Simpson,
stretcher-bearer, found a stray, terrified donkey.
Soon, man and donkey became a familiar sight to the
soldiers. Simpson had trained the donkey to carry
wounded and Donkey was as sure-footed and as
steadfast as the man. His small round hooves picked
a course over the shell-pocked slopes where shifting
earth churned into ankle-deep mud during rain, and
then he plodded undaunted over the rocky hillocks
and treeless ridges. Acrid smoke and dust stung eyes,
throats, then lungs. Machine gun clatter all but wiped
out the sound of Simpson's encouraging voice. Gren-
ades exploded. Shells burst. Simpson and Donkey
saved many lives, patiently, cheerfully.

Then, there were two donkeys. Simpson had found a second stray to train. And so, three weeks passed. "Keep me a big dinner!" Jack Simpson shouted to the camp cook as the three of them moved out one dawn. There was no time for breakfast and no dinner for Simpson. Returning with two wounded that morning he was killed by a machine gun bullet.

"He was an ordinary sort of bloke," soldiers said. A quiet man. A selfless man. His courage was not recorded in the list of military honours. Jack Simpson, the man with the donkey, is remembered nevertheless, for his courage.

Boisterous singing often covered anguish and kept spirits high during war-time when there was little to sing about.

> And the moon shines bright on Charlie Chaplin,
> His boots are cracklin'
> For the want of blackenin',
> And his little baggy trousers need some mendin'
> Before we send him
> To the Dardanelles.

> Sung to the melody of *Red Wing*.

A song still remembered, *Mademoiselle from Armentieres*, came into being during heavy fighting in France. Armentieres was a small town nearby.

And children sang ...

> Mademoiselle from Armentieres,
> *Parley vous!*
> Mademoiselle from Armentieres,
> *Parley vous!*
> Mademoiselle from Armentieres
> Hasn't been kissed for fifty years,
> *Inky pinky parley vous!*

The war ended in November 1918. During that joyous week, May Gibb's very Australian Gumnut babies, Snugglepot and Cuddlepie first appeared. They soon became firm favourites with Australian children and have remained in print ever since.

After the war many fatherless Australian children were cared for by Legacy, and almost every child for the next twenty odd years learned by heart a poem that had been written by a young Canadian doctor who died in France. The war had lasted four years.

IN FLANDERS' FIELDS

In Flanders' fields the poppies blow
Between the crosses, row on row
That mark our place; and in the sky
The larks, still bravely singing, fly
Scarce heard amid the guns below.

We are the Dead. Short days ago
We loved, felt dawn, saw sunset glow,
Loved and were loved, and now we lie
In Flanders' fields.

Take up our quarrel with the foe;
To you from failing hands we throw
The torch; be yours to hold it high
If ye break faith with us who die
We shall not sleep, though poppies grow
In Flanders' fields.

John Macrae

BREAD AND DRIPPIN' DAYS

On the heels of the war stalked years of massive unemploy-
ment and hardship when hungry children were fed 'bread and
drippin', bread spread with dripping instead of butter.

The school leaving age rose to fourteen years. School uniforms also became compulsory when many children had no
shoes, or wore heels square from billy-cart braking, or soles
thin from hop-scotch and skipping games.

I KNOW A FELLAH

I know a fellah who's double jointed,
Sally kissed him and he was disappointed.
All right, Sally, I'll tell your mother
How many times, did you kiss that fellah?
One, two, three, etc.

This rhyme was used by someone skipping with her rope, or
a long rope tied up securely with a 'turner', or two people
turning the rope. The rhyme ends with a *peppers* count.
The next two games need several children skipping together.

All in together (*children run into turning rope*)
This cold weather.
I saw a nanny goat
Putting on a petticoat.
Shoot! Bang! Fire!
All run out! (*skippers run out and game begins again.*)

Skippers run in and out of the rope at random for this rhyme,
chanting, of course. If someone is too slow then O. U. T. It's
her turn to turn the rope, at one or the other end. The same
penalty if someone jumps on the rope, trips or falls over.

Five, ten, fifteen, twenty
No one leave this rope empty.

SATURDEE ARVO'S FLICKS

This was the time when women's and girls' dresses suddenly and sensibly were lopped off at the knees, and there were mind-boggling solo plane flights from Britain to Australia.

It was the great time of films — the talkies and Shirley Temple, child star. Earlier films had been silently screened while someone thumped a piano in the cinema to create mood music.

Saturday afternoons were reserved especially for children's rip-roaring films and suspense serials. No sane adult went to 'the flicks on Saturdee arvo'. Kids booed the villians, cheered favourites, hissed lovers and shouted advice to the screen, and one of the best loved screen idols was Charles Chaplin.

CHARLIE'S SKIPPING RHYME

Charlie Chaplin went to France
To teach the girls how to dance.
How many girls did he teach —
One, two, three, four, etc.

SHIRLEY TEMPLE

Shirley Temple is a STAR. S-T-A-R
She can do the rumba,
She can do the kicks,
She can do the twirley-wirley
She can do the splits!

Shirley from 'Heidi' (1937)

Shirley from 'Baby Burlesks' (1931)

Shirley from 'Little Miss Broadway' (1938)

Mickey Mouse was a famous cartoon character with a regular Saturday afternoon appearance at the cinemas. He also had a skipping rhyme. The child wearing the named colour is supposed to join the skipper. The game keeps going until no one else can possibly fit under the rope.

MICKY MOUSE BOUGHT A HOUSE

Micky Mouse bought a house.
What colour did he paint it.
B - L - U - E. (*Or some other colour*)
Have you got it on you?

This was also the great time of comic books and radio. Fathers sat up all night listening to static-filled broadcasts of test cricket matches being played in England. There were serials and sessions especially for children. And people now often had proper bathrooms and food preserving ice-chests with an ice-man regularly clomping through Mum's kitchen with a block of ice perched on a shoulder on top of a hessian bag. The ice-chests kept milk sweet, meat fresh and set jellies! So, there was jelly and cream for second course, cherries in jelly, jelly and custard, jelly cake and 'punch in the belly jelly'.

131

The vogue for jelly combined strangely with aeroplanes in a song to advertise the dessert.

AEROPLANE JELLY SONG

I've got a song that won't take very long,
Quite a good sort of note if you strike it . . .
It's something to eat, and I think it's quite sweet
And I know you're going to like it.
I like Aeroplane jelly,
Aeroplane jelly for me.
I like it for dinner,
I like it for tea,
A little each day is a good recipe.
The quality's high as the name will imply,
And it's made from pure fruits,
One more reason why
I like Aeroplane jelly,
Aeroplane jelly for me.

However, a spindly little cartoon character from the 'flicks' owed his surprising muscles and super strength to eating spinach straight out of a tin. Popeye the sailorman had his own song that he gruffly sang from his boots, but children had their own version, too.

POPEYE

I'm Popeye, the garbage-man,
I'm Popeye, the garbage-man,
I like to go swimmin'
With bow-legged women.
I'm Popeye, the garbage-man!

Popeye's friend was flat-footed, skinny Olive-oil. Later, they had a baby who never seemed to grow any older and perpetually crawled about in a hampering nightdress. And the baby's name? Sweetpea. All three were world famous.

Blinky Bill was not. Being a koala he was forbidden to leave Australia in those days, but Miss Pimm would have sent him to the zoo when she tried to catch him in her shop. Blinky had helped himself to peppermints. When she discovered him he hid in a tin of biscuits, then a sack of potatoes. He popped out. She saw him ...

NAUGHTY ESCAPADES

"Stop! Stop! I tell you," she screamed. But Blinky had no idea of stopping. He popped in and out of corners, over tins, under bags, and Miss Pimm after him. It was a terrible scuttle and the whole shop seemed to shake. Bottles and tins rattled on the shelves, the door banged, papers flew everywhere, and in the middle of all the din Miss Pimm tripped over a broom that was standing against the counter.

Down she fell, box and all. The clatter was dreadful and her cries were worse. Blinky was terrified. How he wished a gum-tree would spring up through the floor. Suddenly, all of a twinkling, he saw a big bin standing open beside him and without any thought of what might be inside, he climbed up the side and flopped in. It was half full of oatmeal. Using both paws as quickly as he could he scratched a hole in the oatmeal, wriggled and wriggled down as far as he could until he was quite hidden; all that could be seen was a little black nose breathing very quickly. He kept his eyes closed very tightly, and felt very uncomfortable all over; but he was safe at last.

Miss Pimm slowly picked herself up. Her side was hurt and her leg was bruised. The box was broken and also the broom handle. She seemed quite dazed and felt her head. Then, holding on to the counter with one hand she limped round the back of it once more.

"You'll die this time, when I get you," and she seemed to choke the words out.

Every tin, every sack, and every box was moved and examined, but no bear was to be found. She didn't stop to have her tea, but went on searching, hour after hour, and all the store had to be tidied up again. After a very long time she locked the door leading on to the roadway, and Blinky, feeling the benefit of his rest and becoming bolder each minute, peeped over the top of the oatmeal bin. He saw Miss Pimm taking a little packet from a case marked "A.S.P.R.O." He popped down again as he felt quite safe in the bin, but he listened with his large ears to any sound she made.

Presently the lights went out, and after mumbling to herself about "the young cub", she went through to the kitchen. Blinky could see the moon shining through the window-panes and he very, very quietly and gently crawled out of the bin. A shower of oatmeal flew over the floor as he landed on his feet and shook his coat and ears, so that oatmeal was everywhere. Right on to the window-ledge he climbed, trod all over the apples in the window that Miss Pimm had so carefully polished, and sat down for a few minutes on a box of chocolates, then noticing more peppermints in the window he pushed a pawful into his mouth and munched away in great content. The window was half way up so he climbed up the side and sat on the open sill, feeling brave and happy. What a tale he would have to tell Snubby when he reached home.

"Click!" The light in the store was on.

Blinky wasted no more time on thoughts. He was off that window-ledge and across the road in a few seconds. He reached the edge of the bush safely and turned round to see what was happening. Miss Pimm stood in front of the store with a big policeman, pointing to the open window, and then they looked across the roadway to the bush where Blinky lay hidden behind a tree.

"Well, it's a pity he got away," Blinky heard the policeman say, "as the Zoo would have paid you well to have had that young bear. I didn't know there were any about here; and I've lived in the district for thirty years."

"I'd have given him gladly to the Zoo and no payment in return," said Miss Pimm savagely, "if they had offered to replace the peppermints and oatmeal."

The next day when some motorists stopped at Miss Pimm's store and bought some biscuits, they wondered why the biscuits had such a strong taste of eucalyptus.

You're supposed to hop not jump!

7 H 8
6
4 5
3
2
1
Base
Aeroplane

4 3 2
5 1
6 8
7
Base
Circle

6 5
7 1 2 4
8 0 9 3
1 2 3
Base
Snail.

HOPSCOTCH

The winter of 1939 was a good season for hopscotch. Like marbles, the game is as old as old, but charts sometimes changed. *Aeroplane hopscotch* was then a modern playground invention.

A chart was chalked on the ground and followed a strict pattern of *scotches*, the lines that enclosed the numbered spaces. One child could play, or any number, but each owned an individual 'lucky' taw. It could be a small tin weighted with sand, a piece of tile or broken china, or a flattish stone. In fact a taw was anything that slid well because the skill was to hop, kicking the taw from space to space, following the numbers. If the taw or a foot touched a scotch, or worse still, knocked another player's taw, then it was back to base to start again in the next round.

After completing the first round it was not the end of the game by any means. Standing at *base* the taw was slid into space 2 then kicked round the hopscotch. Round again and round again until all the numbered spaces had been used in turn. A game of hopscotch could go on and on. A rest could be taken only at *home*.

You could make up your variations of the game or the charts. Maybe a rocket hopscotch. Incidentally, in aeroplane hopscotch players stood astride across the wings, that is for spaces 4 and 5, then 7 and 8.

WAR AGAIN

Tragically, before hopscotch was discarded that year, children were recognizing the silhouettes of lethal planes — the bombers and fighters of the Second World War.

Winter was fading into spring when war broke out. Australia joined Britain and France against Germany when Poland was invaded.

CHILDREN'S CRUSADE

In 'thirty nine in Poland
There was a bloody fight
And many a town and village
Turned to waste land over night...

Snow fell, as they related
In a certain eastern town
How a new crusade of children
In Poland had begun.

For all along the highways
Troops of hungry children roamed
And gathered to them others
Who stood by ruined homes...

In a coat with a velvet collar
A little Jew was dressed
He had been reared on white bread
But he marched with the rest...

They had a funeral besides
Two Poles and two Germans carried
The boy with the velvet collar
To the place where he was buried.

Grief. Sorrow. No Australian family seemed to be left untouched. Adults tried to keep children's lives as normal as possible. Just as they had had playground rhymes about Kaiser Bill, the children created innumerable verses about Hitler. This one was sung to the melody of *Whistle while you work* from the film, *Snow White*.

WHISTLE WHILE YOU WORK

> Whistle while you work
> Hitler bought a shirt,
> Mussolini wore it,
> Churchill tore it.
> Whistle while you work.

The Japanese bombed Pearl Harbour and the United States joined the allies. Rationing and shortages came and Santa Claus almost disappeared. Darwin and Sydney Harbour were attacked. Children made up more rhymes, including this *counting out* one.

EENA, MEENA, MINA, MO

> Eena, meena, mina, mo,
> Catch old Tojo by the toe.
> If he hollers, let him say,
> 'I surrender, U. S. A.'
> O. U. T. spells *out!*.

And soldiers bellowed, bands played and people sang ...

THE QUARTERMASTER'S STORES
English Traditional

There were rats, rats big as bloom-in' cats In the
stores, in the stores, There were rats, rats
Ly - ing round on mats In the Quar - ter - mas - ter's

Chorus

stores. My eyes are dim, I can - not see, I
have not brought my specs with me I have not
brought my specs with me.

There was steak, steak
Tough as cattle cake
In the stores, in the stores.
There was steak, steak
To give you belly ache
In the Quartermaster's stores.

There was bread, bread
Harder than your head
In the stores, in the stores.
There was bread, bread
Just like lumps of lead
In the Quartermaster's stores.

Make up as many verses as you like — the more nonsense the
better. Nonsense helped during those grim days.

V FOR VICTORY

V for victory, dot-dot-dot-dash,
Hitler lost his old moustache.
If you find it let him know,
And he'll give you lots of dough.

Horrific explosions of atomic bombs on Hiroshima and Nagasaki, in Japan, ended the Second World War. Soon afterwards, Australia began to welcome refugees, then many migrants from other countries, and it has continued to do so since.

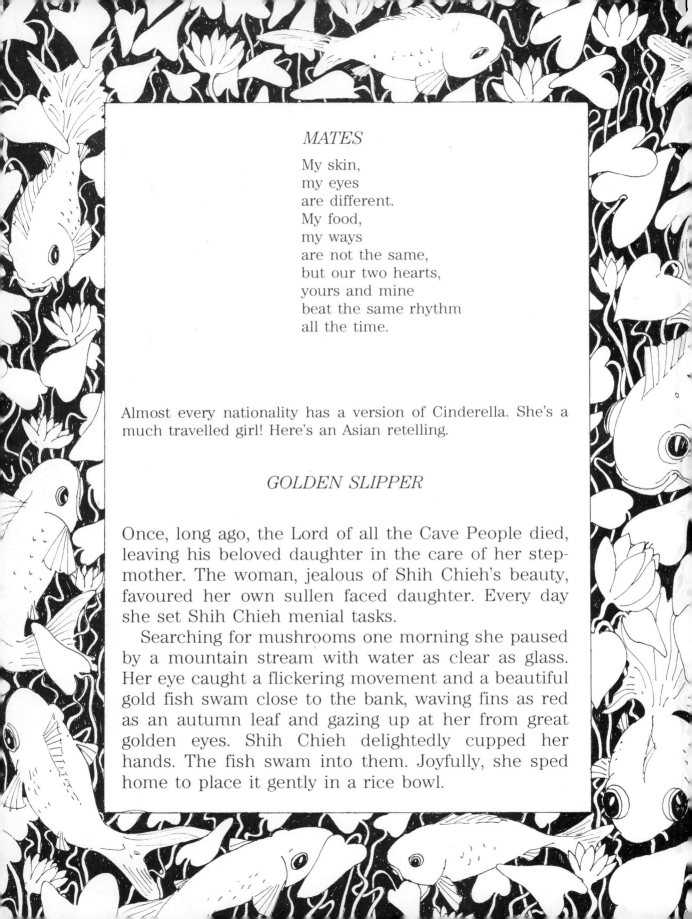

MATES

My skin,
my eyes
are different.
My food,
my ways
are not the same,
but our two hearts,
yours and mine
beat the same rhythm
all the time.

Almost every nationality has a version of Cinderella. She's a much travelled girl! Here's an Asian retelling.

GOLDEN SLIPPER

Once, long ago, the Lord of all the Cave People died, leaving his beloved daughter in the care of her step-mother. The woman, jealous of Shih Chieh's beauty, favoured her own sullen faced daughter. Every day she set Shih Chieh menial tasks.

Searching for mushrooms one morning she paused by a mountain stream with water as clear as glass. Her eye caught a flickering movement and a beautiful gold fish swam close to the bank, waving fins as red as an autumn leaf and gazing up at her from great golden eyes. Shih Chieh delightedly cupped her hands. The fish swam into them. Joyfully, she sped home to place it gently in a rice bowl.

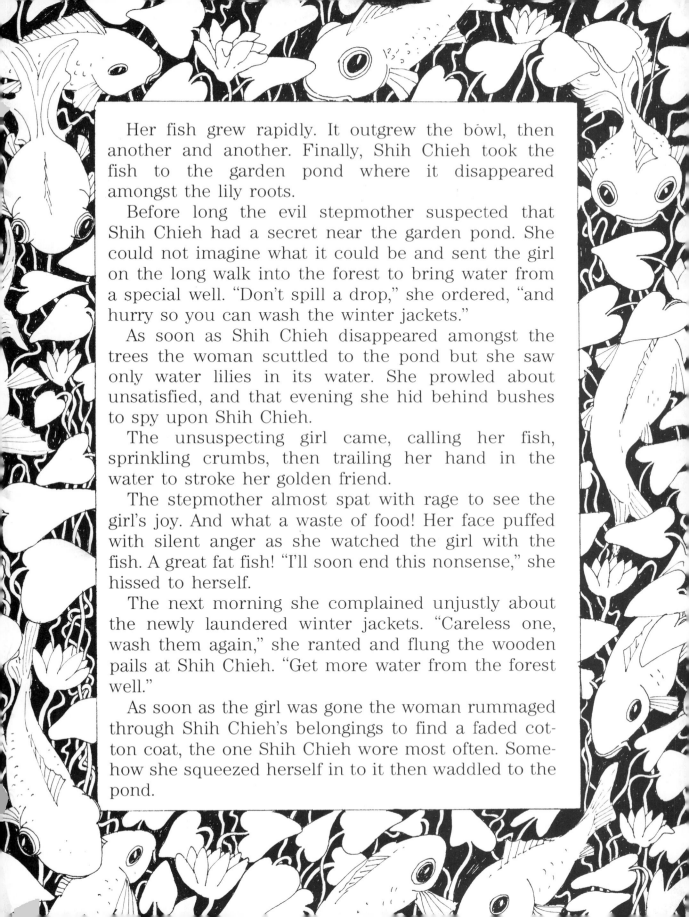

Her fish grew rapidly. It outgrew the bowl, then another and another. Finally, Shih Chieh took the fish to the garden pond where it disappeared amongst the lily roots.

Before long the evil stepmother suspected that Shih Chieh had a secret near the garden pond. She could not imagine what it could be and sent the girl on the long walk into the forest to bring water from a special well. "Don't spill a drop," she ordered, "and hurry so you can wash the winter jackets."

As soon as Shih Chieh disappeared amongst the trees the woman scuttled to the pond but she saw only water lilies in its water. She prowled about unsatisfied, and that evening she hid behind bushes to spy upon Shih Chieh.

The unsuspecting girl came, calling her fish, sprinkling crumbs, then trailing her hand in the water to stroke her golden friend.

The stepmother almost spat with rage to see the girl's joy. And what a waste of food! Her face puffed with silent anger as she watched the girl with the fish. A great fat fish! "I'll soon end this nonsense," she hissed to herself.

The next morning she complained unjustly about the newly laundered winter jackets. "Careless one, wash them again," she ranted and flung the wooden pails at Shih Chieh. "Get more water from the forest well."

As soon as the girl was gone the woman rummaged through Shih Chieh's belongings to find a faded cotton coat, the one Shih Chieh wore most often. Somehow she squeezed herself in to it then waddled to the pond.

"Fish, fish!" she called, imitating Shih Chieh's soft
voice. "Golden fish!" she sang and dangled her hand
in the water so that the fish would recognize the
sleeve of Shih Chieh's jacket.

He swam to the surface in a swirl of red fins and
before his head could break through the water she
pulled a dagger from her sleeve and stabbed.
Triumphantly she carried the body to the house, then
cooked and ate her victim. The fragile, narrow bones
were tossed on the garbage mound amongst cabbage
leaves.

That evening Shih Chieh called to her friend in
vain. She called until she realized that he was not in
the pond. Bewildered she sat on its edge, staring
down at the water for a long moment. Then, she felt
the presence of someone nearby. Her eyes flew
upwards into the face of a stranger. A most peculiar
person with untidy hair and clothes of hessian. A very
small person who said bluntly, "Your stepmother
killed the fish. She threw its bones in the garbage.
Don't weep, child," he added when sobs wracked Shih
Chieh. He came closer, touching her bowed head,
whispering gently. "Your kindness released magic.
Every wish you make will be granted."

Shih Chieh hardly heard and when she did lift her
blurred eyes the Strange One had disappeared. She
called and searched but there was no trace of him.
Had he been there at all? He seemed to belong to a
dream.

She ran to the waste mound. She found the half-
buried bones. Delicate. Snow-white. Fragile. Shih
Chieh cradled them in her hands, carried them back

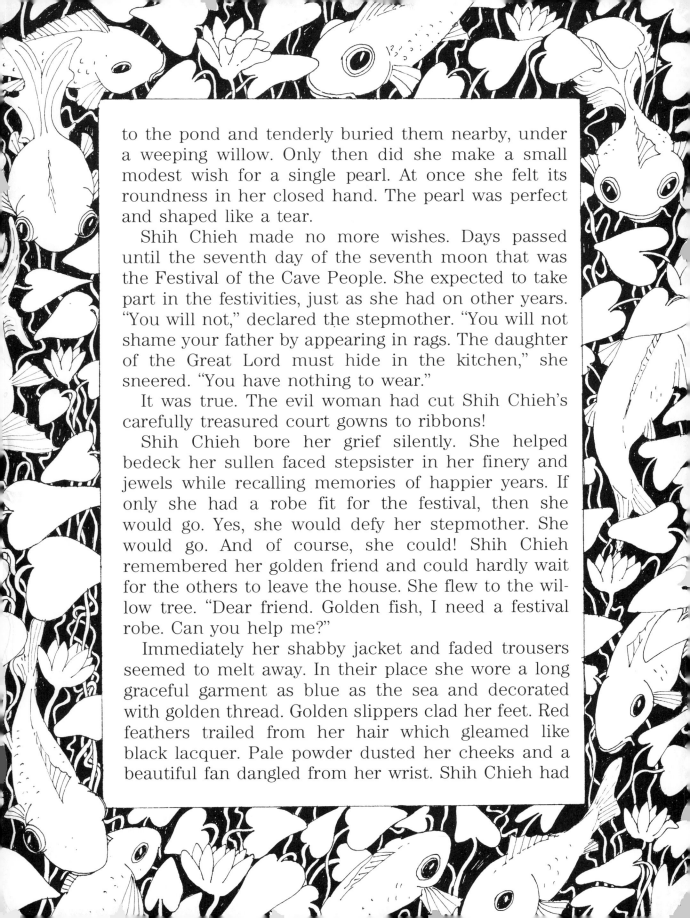

to the pond and tenderly buried them nearby, under
a weeping willow. Only then did she make a small
modest wish for a single pearl. At once she felt its
roundness in her closed hand. The pearl was perfect
and shaped like a tear.

Shih Chieh made no more wishes. Days passed
until the seventh day of the seventh moon that was
the Festival of the Cave People. She expected to take
part in the festivities, just as she had on other years.
"You will not," declared the stepmother. "You will not
shame your father by appearing in rags. The daughter
of the Great Lord must hide in the kitchen," she
sneered. "You have nothing to wear."

It was true. The evil woman had cut Shih Chieh's
carefully treasured court gowns to ribbons!

Shih Chieh bore her grief silently. She helped
bedeck her sullen faced stepsister in her finery and
jewels while recalling memories of happier years. If
only she had a robe fit for the festival, then she
would go. Yes, she would defy her stepmother. She
would go. And of course, she could! Shih Chieh
remembered her golden friend and could hardly wait
for the others to leave the house. She flew to the willow tree. "Dear friend. Golden fish, I need a festival
robe. Can you help me?"

Immediately her shabby jacket and faded trousers
seemed to melt away. In their place she wore a long
graceful garment as blue as the sea and decorated
with golden thread. Golden slippers clad her feet. Red
feathers trailed from her hair which gleamed like
black lacquer. Pale powder dusted her cheeks and a
beautiful fan dangled from her wrist. Shih Chieh had

no mirror to reflect her beauty but she looked lovelier than any flower as she hurried across the fields.

At the festival everyone admired Shih Chieh, including the sullen faced one. "Who is that?" she scowled at her mother. "She looks like Shih Chieh, only she's beautiful. You don't suppose it is Shih Chieh?"

The stepmother's mean eyes fastened on Shih Chieh and the girl became aware of her rude stare. She trembled, not knowing that the woman was declaring, "Of course not. Shih Chieh is at home in the kitchen." And she continued to stare covetously at the sea-blue gown and golden slippers, wishing her daughter looked as lovely. Shih Chieh was rapidly growing nervous, then alarmed. In the end she slipped away, weaving through the crowds, hurrying, hurrying, trying to escape the evil prying eyes.

She tripped on a step. A golden slipper wrenched from her foot, and, too agitated to retrieve it, Shih Chieh ran on. The slipper lay unnoticed until a strange small man with tousled hair and hessian clothes picked it up.

In the meantime, Shih Chieh reached home and when the others eventually returned she was asleep under her mat. "The beauty at the festival certainly was not our kitchen girl," sneered the stepmother. "What a thing to fancy! She's no more than a bundle of rags."

Little did the stepmother know that a mysterious and small person had gained audience with the Emperor and was presenting him with a golden slipper. The Emperor turned it over and over in his

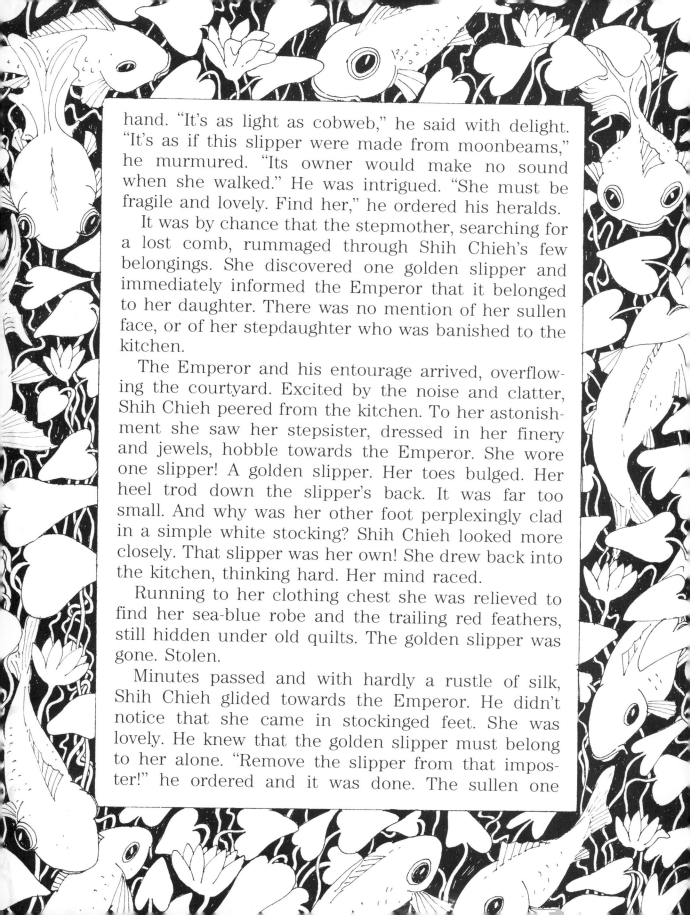

hand. "It's as light as cobweb," he said with delight. "It's as if this slipper were made from moonbeams," he murmured. "Its owner would make no sound when she walked." He was intrigued. "She must be fragile and lovely. Find her," he ordered his heralds.

It was by chance that the stepmother, searching for a lost comb, rummaged through Shih Chieh's few belongings. She discovered one golden slipper and immediately informed the Emperor that it belonged to her daughter. There was no mention of her sullen face, or of her stepdaughter who was banished to the kitchen.

The Emperor and his entourage arrived, overflowing the courtyard. Excited by the noise and clatter, Shih Chieh peered from the kitchen. To her astonishment she saw her stepsister, dressed in her finery and jewels, hobble towards the Emperor. She wore one slipper! A golden slipper. Her toes bulged. Her heel trod down the slipper's back. It was far too small. And why was her other foot perplexingly clad in a simple white stocking? Shih Chieh looked more closely. That slipper was her own! She drew back into the kitchen, thinking hard. Her mind raced.

Running to her clothing chest she was relieved to find her sea-blue robe and the trailing red feathers, still hidden under old quilts. The golden slipper was gone. Stolen.

Minutes passed and with hardly a rustle of silk, Shih Chieh glided towards the Emperor. He didn't notice that she came in stockinged feet. She was lovely. He knew that the golden slipper must belong to her alone. "Remove the slipper from that imposter!" he ordered and it was done. The sullen one screamed and her mother was beside herself with rage. Had the Emperor been aware of their shocking behaviour he would have had their heads chopped off at once. Fortunately for them he was aware only of Shih Chieh and wanted to carry her off to his palace.

Shih Chieh was willing to go, but first she insisted upon telling him of the golden fish. She was to carry the fragile bones away with her, inside a box lined with crimson silk. It was buried in the most beautiful part of the Emperor's garden.

A more modern version of Cinderella was born in an Australian playground.

> Cinderella dressed in yella,
> Went downstairs to meet her fella,
> On the way her panties busted,
> How many people were disgusted?

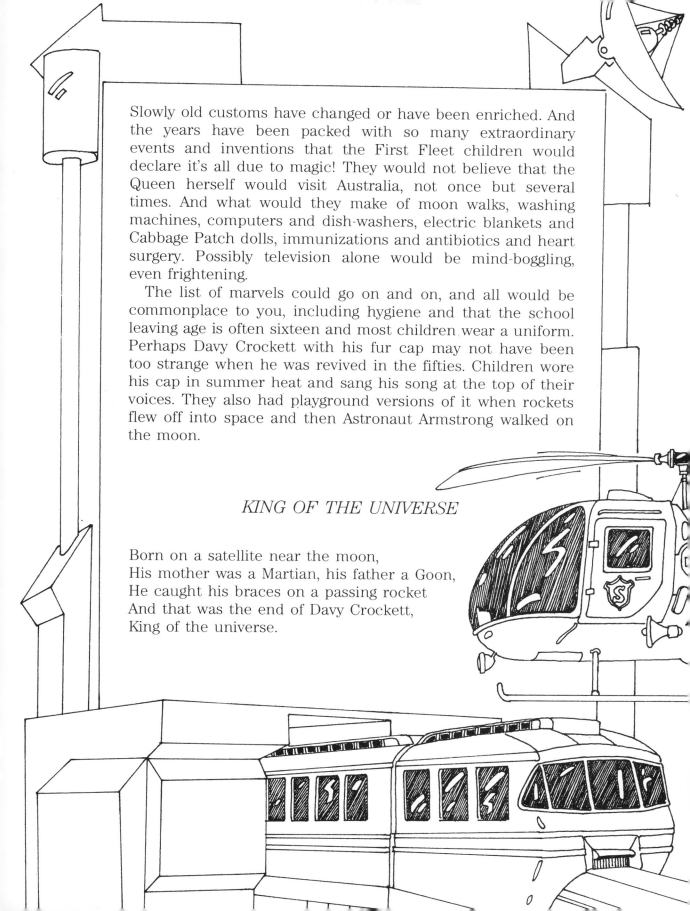

Slowly old customs have changed or have been enriched. And the years have been packed with so many extraordinary events and inventions that the First Fleet children would declare it's all due to magic! They would not believe that the Queen herself would visit Australia, not once but several times. And what would they make of moon walks, washing machines, computers and dish-washers, electric blankets and Cabbage Patch dolls, immunizations and antibiotics and heart surgery. Possibly television alone would be mind-boggling, even frightening.

The list of marvels could go on and on, and all would be commonplace to you, including hygiene and that the school leaving age is often sixteen and most children wear a uniform. Perhaps Davy Crockett with his fur cap may not have been too strange when he was revived in the fifties. Children wore his cap in summer heat and sang his song at the top of their voices. They also had playground versions of it when rockets flew off into space and then Astronaut Armstrong walked on the moon.

KING OF THE UNIVERSE

Born on a satellite near the moon,
His mother was a Martian, his father a Goon,
He caught his braces on a passing rocket
And that was the end of Davy Crockett,
King of the universe.

From outer space, our world is beautiful, lonely and small. Everything that lives on it, must share it. And recent years have brought efforts to conserve our world. Both adults and children bring positive action and thoughtfulness that are messages of hope for the future in a time of conflict, in a time of fear of possible destruction from nuclear warfare.

SADAKO

Sadako was a very little girl living in Hiroshima when an atomic bomb dropped by Americans exploded and ended the war with Japan, in 1945. Ten years later Sadako died as a result of the radiation from the bomb. Her story of courage is true. It came to Australia in 1981 for all children to share, and here we meet Sadako, in hospital, just after she realises that she has "the atom bomb disease".

THE GOLDEN CRANE

The next morning Sadako woke up slowly. She listened for the familiar sounds of her mother making breakfast, but there were only the new and different sounds of a hospital. Sadako sighed. She had hoped that yesterday was just a bad dream. It was even more real when Nurse Yasunaga came in to give her an injection.

"Getting shots is part of being in hospital," the plump nurse said briskly. "You'll get used to it."

"I just want the sickness to be over with," Sadako said unhappily, "so I can go home."

That afternoon Chizuko was Sadako's first visitor. She smiled mysteriously as she held something behind her back. "Shut your eyes," she said. While Sadako squinted her eyes tightly shut, Chizuko put some pieces of paper and scissors on the bed. "Now you can look," she said.

"What is it?" Sadako asked, staring at the paper.

Chizuko was pleased with herself. "I've figured out a way for you to get well," she said proudly. "Watch!" She cut a piece of gold paper into a large square. In a short time she had folded it over and over into a beautiful crane.

Sadako was puzzled. "But how can that paper bird make me well?"

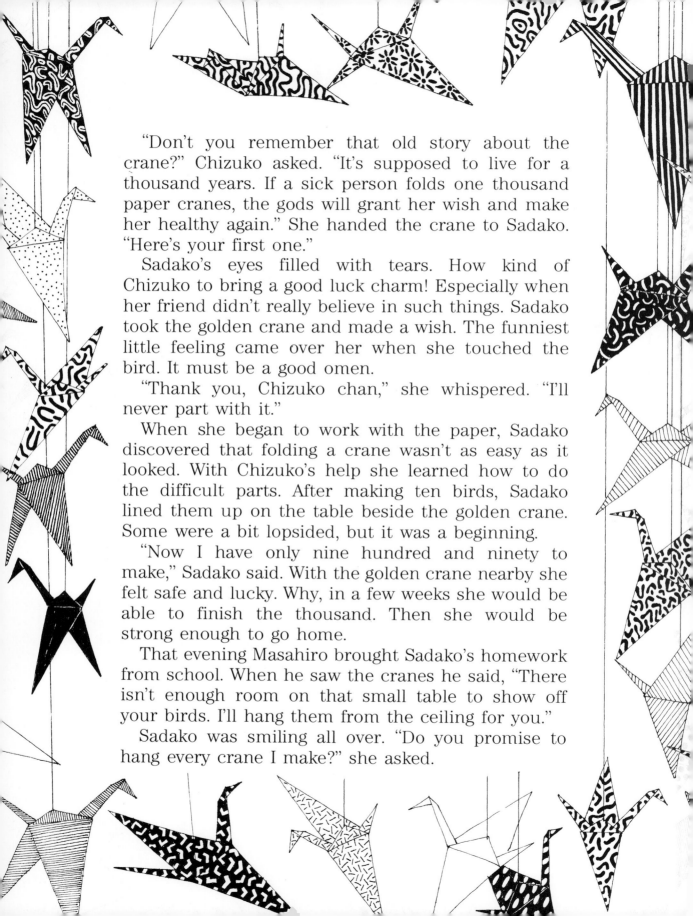

"Don't you remember that old story about the crane?" Chizuko asked. "It's supposed to live for a thousand years. If a sick person folds one thousand paper cranes, the gods will grant her wish and make her healthy again." She handed the crane to Sadako. "Here's your first one."

Sadako's eyes filled with tears. How kind of Chizuko to bring a good luck charm! Especially when her friend didn't really believe in such things. Sadako took the golden crane and made a wish. The funniest little feeling came over her when she touched the bird. It must be a good omen.

"Thank you, Chizuko chan," she whispered. "I'll never part with it."

When she began to work with the paper, Sadako discovered that folding a crane wasn't as easy as it looked. With Chizuko's help she learned how to do the difficult parts. After making ten birds, Sadako lined them up on the table beside the golden crane. Some were a bit lopsided, but it was a beginning.

"Now I have only nine hundred and ninety to make," Sadako said. With the golden crane nearby she felt safe and lucky. Why, in a few weeks she would be able to finish the thousand. Then she would be strong enough to go home.

That evening Masahiro brought Sadako's homework from school. When he saw the cranes he said, "There isn't enough room on that small table to show off your birds. I'll hang them from the ceiling for you."

Sadako was smiling all over. "Do you promise to hang every crane I make?" she asked.

Masahiro promised.

"That's fine!" Sadako said, her eyes twinkling with mischief. "Then you'll hang the whole thousand?"

"A thousand!" Her brother groaned. "You're joking!"

Sadako told him the story of the cranes.

Masahiro ran a hand through his straight black hair. "You tricked me!" he said with a grin. "But I'll do it anyhow." He borrowed some thread and tacks from Nurse Yasunaga and hung the first ten cranes. The golden crane stayed in its place of honour on the table.

After supper Mrs Sasaki brought Mitsue and Eiji to the hospital. Everyone was surprised to see the birds. They reminded Mrs Sasaki of a famous old poem:

> Out of coloured paper, cranes
> come flying into
> our house.

Mitsue and Eiji liked the golden crane best. But Mrs Sasaki chose the tiniest one made of fancy green paper with pink parasols on it. "This is my choice," she said, "because small ones are the most difficult to make."

After visiting hours it was lonely in the hospital room. So lonely that Sadako folded more cranes to keep up her courage.

Eleven ... I wish I'd get better.
Twelve ... I wish I'd get better ...

Sadako did feel better for a while and she kept on making paper cranes. Six hundred and forty-four cranes! Her school friends made the rest after Sadako's death, and the little girl lives on in the memories of many because her story flew about Japan and then over the seas and on to you. Her statue stands in the Hiroshima Peace Park. She holds out her golden crane to the world's children. Many come, especially on Peace Day that falls on August 6th, and they leave tokens of folded paper cranes.

This is our cry
this is our prayer
peace in the world.

PAPER CRANES

You can make paper cranes, too. Be patient. You can do it!
Here's a few tips to keep — always fold the paper *away* from
the cut edge. Otherwise, the crane won't open up. And try to
keep your folds as even as you can.
One last thing — remember to repeat each pair of folds on the
reverse side.

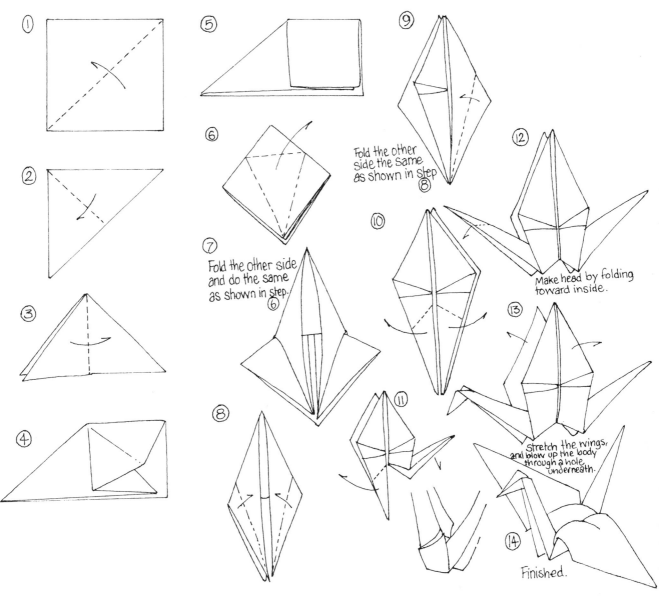

① ② ③ ④ ⑤

⑥

⑦ Fold the other side and do the same as shown in step ⑥

⑧

⑨ Fold the other side the same as shown in step ⑧

⑩

⑪

⑫ Make head by folding toward inside.

⑬ Stretch the wings, and blow up the body through a hole underneath.

⑭ Finished.

YOUR TIME

Your time is a century ending
and the new one beginning.
Your time is computers, satellites and Halley's comet.
Your time is recognition of Aboriginal culture, and books of
every kind.

Treasure your time.
Open your ears,
Your heart, your eyes.
Look! Feel! Hear!
Cherish what you find.
Wunnun ...
It is the time of sharing.

Sally Atkins belongs to your time. An Australian, she was seventeen years old when she wrote ...

OUR TOMORROW

Let's think of the future
and the things it may with hold.
Let's think of our tomorrow
and hope we will grow old.

INDEX

THE END